D1708769

A MEMOIR

NIGHT GOBLINS

JT GREGORY

ILLUSTRATED BY ANTOINE BOURALY

The Ditch Kitty

This is a work of creative nonfiction. And while nonfiction is typically written from memory, it's important to note that our ability to remember things is not without flaws. However, the following events have been portrayed to the best of JT Gregory's memory, and all of the stories in this book are true (except some names and identifying details that have been changed to protect the privacy of the people involved).

Printed in Canada

First Printing, 2020

ISBN 978-1-7352947-0-4 (hardcover)
ISBN 978-1-7352947-1-1 (paperback)
ISBN 978-1-7352947-2-8 (ebook)

Lunarus Publishing
PO Box 470
Auburn, MI 48725

www.jtgregory.com

For Felipe

PROLOGUE

*T*he Kid's like three beers in—well, three beers and however many shots have come to the table. His companions are in much deeper than that, he thinks; hell, he's just treading water, comparatively. But isn't this what all drunk people think, that everyone is much drunker than they are? Fact of the matter is, if you're in a bar this close to last call, you're probably just as drunk as everyone around you, no matter how much you deny it. And if there's one thing a drunk likes to do, it's deny his perceived level of drunkenness. Which is a fucking farce. And everybody knows it.

So it's not quite last call, right, but the lighting is low like that, over-head, the light at the bar, all of it soft and warm and fuzzy kinda. It's the sort of bar with a bunch of regulars, everybody seems to be on a first-name basis, i.e. Hey Jim, your usual? And Jim says yep and to put it on his tab, and he takes his usual to a seat right in front of this little stage, where there's a DJ playing All The Greatest Hits or something and a little karaoke machine for when people get drunk enough to get up on the stage and belt out the lyrics to one of their favorite songs, and badly so. There's a little makeshift dance floor, or rather, a piece of floor that several people have deemed worthy of some rug-cutting, tables and chairs pushed to the side, and what a sight to behold, it's alive and writhing and wet, or like damp, these people dancing in such close proximity to one another, sweaty locks of hair whipping and shiny forearms seesawing back and forth and hips and lips gyrating almost angrily. The walls seem to pulsate along with the DJ's choice of deep booming music, shimmying and shaking right along with the small collection of drunkards teetering toward and away from each other in some end-of-the-night mating ritual of sorts.

And so The Kid is talking to some guy, this man with no face, and all The Kid hears when he opens his mouth is static, soft-soft-soft static, nothing like the horror-movie equivalent. He doesn't know what they're talking about, probably nothing, definitely nothing, because what sorta substance can a drunk conversation have? And eventually The Kid just gives up on the whole thing, abruptly decides that he's had enough, abruptly turns, abruptly inserts himself into whatever conversation his drunk friends are having, and just ignores the static behind him, buzz-buzz-buzzing static, no fucking face, what kinda guy has no face.

3

The Kid's friends, though, their faces are out there and very open, as drunk faces are so wont to be, and they're all teetering on the edge of sweat. They glisten, their cheeks and their foreheads, their eyes, their teeth flashing with each word and smile and drunken laugh. The pitcher of beer in the middle of the table drains like it's got a crack somewhere in its glass body, and the pitcher of beer becomes pitchers of beer and shots and an order of loaded nachos, and maybe some more beers, wait—no. No more pitchers, just a round for everybody. And one more shot, just one more.

Okay. Maybe another. It's only one-thirty.

The Kid takes another sip of beer.

Paul is sitting across from The Kid, he's sitting with his forearms crossed in front of him, two hairy hams, two pale boulders covered in tattoos that look like cave drawings, and his skin is wrapped around his body almost reluctantly, the way skin looks when someone's gained weight and then lost some and then gained it back. He's shaped like a sandbag, Paul is, but an old one, a sandbag that's seen a couple tours, so not crisp and full of new sand, but like weathered in a way that reminds The Kid of cloudless skies and a sun that moves too slowly and burns too bright, not the same sun you might see anywhere, not home, not nowhere. Paul's hair is as high and tight as it can be without making the full transition to chrome dome, and he's dressed in clothes with skulls on them. And he laughs, loudly, joyously, and he drinks.

We all drink.

Then there's Lauren, The Kid's current sig-other, she's a big smile with long legs, with thick brown hair that looks almost blonde, with lips the color of stolen rubies, with eyes the color of the aforementioned cloudless skies, and the relationship is new enough that The Kid still shivers a little when her arm accidentally touches his, that electric shock; and Kayla, Paul's girl, she's glowing softly, her skin pale, a number of piercings dotting her face and glinting sharply every now and then, like when she tosses her head and laughs, showing a set of too-white teeth just beneath a set of glasses that have seen better days.

And whaddya know, speaking of drunk idiots, somebody's finally shucked back enough drinks to hop up on the stage. Or maybe this guy thinks everybody else is finally drunk enough to listen to him sing without booing him to fuck and back, who knows, maybe it's a little bit of both, one drunk idiot standing up in front of a bunch of other drunk idiots, doing and saying drunk-idiot shit like, This one's for the ladies in the house, *and someone makes a sound like a kicked hyena in the back, some people laugh, and some of the aforementioned ladies, they raise their glasses in the air and mimic the hyena in the back, crowing victoriously as if they've just made a long-awaited kill out on the Serengeti. Or maybe he raises his drink, he's brought it up there with him, and maybe he toasts something that everybody can relate to,* Here's to getting shit-wasted, here's to all those poor sufferers in third-worlds, here's to FUCK THE ESTABLISH- MENT. *Then everybody cheers, and this guy, he mutters his song choice to the DJ and the DJ tunes it up and the guy says something like,* SING ALONG IF YOU KNOW IT, *and probably some people do and they stand up and start swaying back and forth, until The Kid feels so much like a part of some weird cult of lemmings that he considers standing up and leaving before they really gather some momentum and toss themselves off the nearest cliff.*

But then Paul's like, Well hey, I've got an idea, let's go back to the *apartments and drink some beers and go swimming or something, and they're all pretty agreeable. So they stand up and somebody not The Kid goes and closes out the tab while The Kid heads outside for a breath o' fresh, pushes his way past the small gathering of moist hyenas cackling and bouncing off each other like so many pinballs, and then the song ends and it's someone else up there, somebody else is singing now, something by Bon Jovi, and it's loud and obnoxious and raucous and—*

It's cool outside, the sorta relieved coolness a landscape takes on in the aftermath of a hot August day. The sky is expressionless above the bustle of hot city lights. The Kid inhales deeply, sucking cool night air in through flared nostrils, filling his lungs to brimming. The tail end of the inhalation, though, it reeks of dried and drying vomit, of cooling tailpipes and hot tires and kicked dust. There's an arc-sodium light buzzing just above The Kid, a vibrating hum, although it's something The Kid can feel moreso than hear, and the light itself is reluctant. Impatient. Annoyed, somehow. And as he exhales, once he finally does, he's able to convince himself that this breath o' fresh has done him a world of good, that he's much more sober than he was when he exited the bar, and that he's as a-okay to drive as he's ever been.

There are two girls hanging out just by the door, smoking and smiling at The Kid suggestively, or in a drunken way meant to come across as suggestive, and so he goes over and says hi, not hi, hey, Well hey, how're y'all? *And their smiles turn a little sour, The Kid thinks, as if maybe they'd been more interested in the idea of him coming over than the actual doing of it, and he suddenly feels awkward, like he's walked into the wrong neighborhood wearing the wrong color skin, that uncomfortable feeling of being seen as more of a something than a someone. So The Kid asks to bum a cigarette, not because he smokes, but because asking for a cigarette and pretending that he does is miles better than standing there with his hands in his pockets, waiting for his friends to come tumbling out of the bar like drunken gymnasts.*

But then the others do come out, falling against the door and lurching out into the parking lot much in the same way as The Kid. Paul trips and almost falls, but to be fair, Kayla's pushing him from behind, thrusting him from the bar as if in response to some protest, maybe a sudden unwillingness to stick with the plan, to leave the bar and get home, driving having yet been specified, and go swimming in the complex's pool, sipping lukewarm beer from a can and bathing beneath the unseen gaze of faraway stars and convincing themselves, probably, that the chlorinated water is much more refreshing than it actually is.

Who's driving?

Me.

Don't you think—

But who should drive though, really. I don't think I can. I can try.

Uh, no. I'm driving.

I think you're too—

I AM DRIVING, *The Kid says, turning away from any further protest and setting off across the small, graveled parking lot, his bleary eyes searching for a bright red truck he's purchased only just recently with what'd been left of the money he'd saved up during his last deployment. He stumbles, but only a little. The gravel beneath his shoes shifts with each step, making for very difficult walking, and perhaps there's a strategy here. Perhaps the gravel is meant to slow them down, the drunks. Perhaps it's there to give them time, give The Kid time to change his mind, to think about what he's about to do, to think and then, perhaps, rethink.*

In the end, gravel and difficulty walking and perhapses aside, this turns out not to be the case.

And then he sees it, the truck, and he's there, The Kid is, and he wrenches the door open in dramatic fashion, almost flourishing his decision to drive. He gets in and smiles at his companions, injecting them with his own drunken confidence, and why not, because The Kid hadn't fallen down on his way to the truck, had he? And besides that, aren't they all pretty drunk? And who among them is willing to take that chance, especially with The Kid already sitting in the driver's seat, smiling and confident and in a bit in a rush, if we're being honest, a bit hurried to get on the road and head back to the apartment complex and grab some extra beers and hit the pool. Who among them? There's no real reason for anyone else to offer their services as a drunk driver. The Kid's got it covered.

So they all get in, Lauren calling shotgun and hopping in the passenger and the other two crowding the back, and The Kid jabs the key into the ignition a little too hard, cranks her up a little too eagerly. Music booms out of the speakers, ringing The Kid's head like a dinner bell. And he leaves it that way, cranked all the way to eleven, and backs out of his parking spot with so much gas that gravel sprays up, peppering the windshields of a few surrounding vehicles like so much thrown buckshot. He slams it into drive, stepping on the gas while turning the wheel to his very immediate right; and he peels out, or rather, would've peeled out if not for the gravel, and exits the parking lot to the tune of distant protest, arms raised in his rearview to indicate quite a few strong what-the-fucks.

The Kid's in deep now. Much deeper than three beers and however many shots came to the table. He's drawn toward the event horizon like a pulled string. The truck roars down the tiny side street, using a lane and a half to do it, and they come to the first stoplight pretty quickly. The Kid thrusts the nose of the truck out into the intersection, and it lurches, it bucks and snorts in ways that perhaps it shouldn't. Laughter fills the truck to brimming, but perhaps more nervous a laughter than normal. There's a car in the turn lane next to The Kid, this guy, he appears drunk too, he's flirting with the beginning of a burnout, the heavy grunting of gas fighting brakes, the sound of dry tires catching on dry pavement, hot tires and hot pavement. The Kid rolls his window down, rolls all the windows down, and throws her into neutral, and he steps on the gas and brake at the same time, his own hot tires catching their own hot pavement, and what ensues is some kinda drunken standoff, him staring at The Kid, and The Kid staring right back, and it's weird and uncomfortable, but fun too. Undulations writhe in The Kid's stomach like a sack of snakes. There's a Don't Tread on Me sticker in the window of the car. And they all shout at each other, back and forth, laughing and glaring intermittently, an inability to settle on anything at all, much less an emotion or a general feeling about oneself.

The intersecting road, it's Bragg Blvd, the name of which reminds The Kid of Monopoly or something, but the blvd itself is nothing like this fun pastime. It's littered with strip clubs, women in there gyrating lazily, the dollar bills sticking to their moist skin for a couple seconds before falling off and fluttering to the ground like damaged butterflies; and too, various fast-food places and used-car lots, and at least one whorehouse, at least one video store where it's rumored a soldier can walk in, no questions asked, and go to the back and stick his cock through a ragged hole in the wall and be fellated by a woman with a mustache; and there's places to buy new stereos for nothing down and no payments for six months, and places to get half-assed haircuts for full price, places to get one's car detailed for the low-low price of one arm and one leg. Bragg Blvd is the bane of Fayetteville's existence, dark and seedy like a rotten grapefruit, and a single wrong turn off the blvd might land some of the more naïve soldiers in places so dark and so seedy that they never make it home, and there are very few what make it back in one piece, mind and body and soul, the same way they came. No one questions it because while the blvd certainly is a bane, it's also a mithridate, serves as a cure for all that ails you, all that's wrong with a body. And this is just the way of things in military towns. It's a hedonistic paradise. In it there is everything. But this is what it takes from you, too. Everything.

And the light flicks green then.

CHAPTER ONE

I'm pedaling down the side of a two-lane, riding the weathered strip of asphalt between the dirty shoulder and the road itself, and the wind is holding me back the way a friend might in the middle of a schoolyard fight, because *he's not worth it* and *you'll get in trouble* and et cetera. I'm dressed appropriately for the mid-Michigan September morning, clothes meant to guard one from the remnants of last night's dip in temperature; but I'm also dressed for success in a collared shirt the color of vacation waters, some nice pants, and a pair of dirty boots, all of it very business casual, until you get to the boots, anyway. It's early, a couple-few hours after the sun's initial push over a horizon that never gets any closer, no matter how hard I pedal against the cool wind buffeting me hither and thither, and the gentle rays are working hard to warm blades of shivering grass, trees that seem to be thinning a little at the temples, and warming me too, if the sweat drip-drip-dripping from my nose is any indication.

"You've gotta be fuckin *kidding* me," I say, muttering to myself and reaching up to wipe my leaking brow, a quick motion meant to mini-mize the potential for mistakes, and I return it to the handlebars just in time to correct the bike away from the steady stream of late-to-workers blowing by me at intervals. The front wheel shimmies and shakes, back and forth, to and fro, making everything a little more interesting than I'm comfortable with, but isn't there something innately uncomfortable about riding a bike comprising pieces from several other bikes? "C'mon, Frank, don't lemme down now."

Frank, as the bike has been dubbed, whines in rusty protest, the sound of oldness and left-out-in-the-rain-ness and unnatural together-ness, and the chain ratchets and pops, shifting Frank from seventh gear to something that feels very less-than-oneish. He's built for neither speed nor comfort, perhaps moreso out of necessity than anything else. A piece here, there, a chain and a new wheel from this pile of garbage, a seat taken from the remnants of someone else's bad luck, and so on. And I do the only thing I can do, I pedal harder, hurling a couple effing-mothers into the gusts of cool wind smacking me in the face like kamikazying summer bugs blindly seeking the sort of honored infamy bugs rarely find.

A semitruck passes then, the horn blaring a needled punch deep into my ear, momentarily reversing the aerodynamic drag to slap me in the back in a *cmon-what's-taking-you-so-long* kind of way. I curse some more, wipe my brow, and I curse again through gritted teeth, my pulse thumping angrily, my hamstrings and adductors and quadriceps and whatever else tensing and releasing and tensing and releasing and tensing, tensing, tensing.

"Fucking *mother!*"

The morning hadn't started off too bad. Sure, it had only been as good as waking up jobless and penniless and hungover can be, as good as drinking instant coffee and eating off-brand oatmeal can be, as scanning Craigslist for job offerings that seemed less murdery than some of the others can be, but it hadn't been terrible, that morning, and it had seemingly taken a turn for the good, the morning and the day and life in general, when I'd found a job posting that seemed rather promising.

Subway is now hiring! Do you enjoy working in a FAST-PACED EVIORNMENT? Are you TEAM-ORIENTED? Are you dedicated to providing our customers with EXCELLENT FOOD, GREAT CUSTOMER SERVICE, and a CLEAN EVIORNMENT? If so, please apply in person at—

And blah blah blah. The ad itself had seemed homey, down to earth in some way, human and folkish in that whomever had written the ad had gone through this much trouble to craft the damn thing, capitalizing this and exclaiming that, and had somehow, whether intentionally or not, misspelled the word *environment*. I didn't think a murderer would have put that much thought into a bait ad only to post it with a misspelled word, and the only sick pervert associated with Subway that I knew had been put behind bars a while ago, hadn't he?

So we'd gotten to the job interview like twenty minutes early, me and Frank, and we'd just sat there for a while outside the place, trying to swallow the very last of my hangover like a handful of grapes covered in super glue, and watching cars pass and worrying, wondering if I've dressed appropriately enough for a job interview at Subway, and how their perception of what was appropriate might differ from my own; and too, wondering if like, I was too early, assuming they'd seen me ride up, assuming they'd assumed it was me, he of the weak and thin resume, he of the out-of-town-accent, and if they were waiting inside, checking their watches intermittently, checking the wall clock intermittently, and comparing the two; and wondering, lastly and most of all, whether showing up on a bike that looked as if it had been stolen from several different places, pieces taken from the gravesites people left near the road, another man's trash and all that, and dressing in what I considered my good jeans and my nicest collared and a pair of work boots, and showing up early, as early as I had, awkwardly early, was enough to show that I did indeed *enjoy working in a FAST-PACED EVIORNMENT,* that I was *TEAM-ORIENTED,* and that I was fully capable of providing their customers with *EXCELLENT FOOD, GREAT CUSTOMER SERVICE, and a CLEAN EVIORNMENT.*

I shake my head and pedal harder. Frank groans, shifting gears for the fuck of it, and shakes his head too.

It hadn't been, ultimately, and that was the whole thing of it. And why? Too many reasons why. There's a sort of servility that comes with attending a job interview, groveling and beseeching mannerisms to which I'm not really accustomed, and who knows, maybe it had showed. She'd sat there across from me, the interviewer, this uncomfortable mask made face-like by the proportionate and symmetrical positioning of eyebrows and eyes and nostrils and lip curvature, and there had been nothing there, on her face, that suggested or hinted at a future for me as a sandwich artist or whatever. And my weak attempts to appear more affable than I really am, more cheery and amicable than your average bear, had fallen flatter than her face, and I'd left with nothing but a *we'll-be-in-touch* and a weak handshake, like shaking hands with a fish, and the feeling, this distinct and unsettling notion, that Frank had a better chance at landing a job in such a *CLEAN EVIORNMENT* than I did.

A car passes with two more in tow, a disjointed snake slithering past at a speed well above the unspoken rule of *9-you're-fine-but-10-you're-mine.* One honks, a sheep-like bleat, and I lift my left hand chest high, finally fed all the way up, and I unfurl the wings of what feels like the most glorious bird to have ever flown.

"Yeah, beep this, you mother—"

And the thing is, riding a bike down the side of the road? It's an art. It takes hawkish concentration to keep that baby steady, centered right there in that sweet spot between the weathered white line and the weathered gravel carpeting the roadside. Do that and you're all but golden. *Don't* do that, and throw in the fact that the bike itself has little to no desire to be riding down the side of the road in the first place, that the bike seems to want nothing more than to throw himself into the raging flow of mid-morning traffic, and what you get is what you get. The suicidal jerking of a barely serviceable front wheel. The corresponding overcorrection made by a hastily placed hand. These things paired oh-so-conveniently with the rusted chain's swan song, a dry popping. And directly afterward, the sad sound of pedals being pedaled without pedaling, as the bike, Frank, finally gives up the ghost, pitching the both of us face-first into the roadside ditch with the words *FAST-PACED* and *TEAM-ORIENTED* and *EXCELLENT FOOD* and *GREAT CUSTOMER SERVICE* and *CLEAN EVIORNMENT, EVIORNMENT, EVIORNMENT* bouncing around the inside of my skull like ping-pong balls.

I just lay there for a minute, staring skyward. A car passes, meeping joyfully. The clouds overhead are thin, their mass embellished across the blue backdrop, stretching into mere afterthoughts as they approach the sun, stealthily teasing, pantomiming the idea of shade as they eclipse, just so, and flit off. The sun glares steadily, a retina-sizzling heat. And I stare back, forcing my eyelids to remain open, and retinas be damned.

It wasn't like I'd truly wanted the job, making sandwiches, sandwich artistry or whatever, that's nobody's dream job. I've been to Subway plenty of times, and believe me when I tell you, there's nothing even vaguely artistic about a meatball sub. And so, maybe not really wanting the damn job had showed; or maybe it had been the way I'd dressed, or rather—and more so—the way I hadn't dressed. Maybe it'd had something to do with Frank, with riding up on a bicycle that seemed to openly mock the very idea of being a reliable mode of transportation; hell, maybe it had been a little bit of everything, one aggravating factor after another, too many to ignore.

Or maybe it'd been the big, fat checkmark next to *Yes* on the part of the application asking me if I've ever been convicted of a felony.

"Reliable," I say, finally conceding my petty staring contest with the sun and closing my eyes against its triumphant glare. The residual effects pulse red and black and hot white behind my eyelids. "You're not very reliable, Frank."

Frank whines, low and distraught, his back tire spinning ineffaciously, *squeak-squeak-squeak*. I sigh. And grimace a little, I can already feel how much this is going to hurt tomorrow.

But it hadn't been about finding some dream job. It usually never is, people work jobs they hate all the time, for any number of reasons. It'd been about *needing* it. Because my dream of writing a book and publishing it and being all I could be and et cetera just hadn't gone the way I thought it might. There's no money in *almost* doing something, but somewhere, somewhen, maybe at the end of the whole process, I'd thought, there's Being Rich and Being Famous and Being An Author, not a measly fucking writer, an actual *author* and all that, some surreal combination of James Patterson and Phillip Meyer, where critical acclaim and assloads of cash and awards would come cascading down like some fortuitous waterfall, and damn the past, and damn the more realistic possibility that I might, in fact, find myself hunting for a minimum-wage job just to pay the bills, and might, in fact, find myself lying prone by the side of the road, squinting my eyes against a September sun and breathing in the smell of passing traffic and listening to the sounds of people looking at me as they drive by, of birds arguing in the trees, of Frank, this unreliable bastard son of a bastard son, still squeaking from his post-accident resting spot a couple yards away, noncommittally half in the roadside ditch and half out.

"Shut up, already," I say, unsure if I'm talking to Frank or myself. I brace myself for the pain and sit up, wincing to my feet awkwardly like it's my first time.

Because none of the aforementioned for-whys were the *real* reason I needed the damn job. The *real* reason being a very big something that'd happened an entire eight months ago, maybe longer, when I'd been *out of prison for about a month, sitting on a stool in the very back of a small pizzeria, his arms crossed on the table in front of him, a nervous sweat building on his forehead, his upper lip, beneath his arms, and he can barely hear her talking over the sound of his own heart thumping madly, pounding against his breastbone like an inmate convinced of his own innocence. The Kid's hands are both cold and sweaty, somehow, as is the very tip of his nose. His mouth is an arid wasteland, his throat, and every swallow is like eating sandpaper. It's a big world, and things have changed, they must have, it's been years. But that's not what scares him. What scares him is how much everything has stayed the same, almost as if he never did what he did, almost as if the past 51 months have been a lie, something he made up in his head. But only almost. Because every breath he takes is a reminder of all of that well-deserved time he spent behind bars, and just because the world hadn't moved when The Kid pushed it doesn't mean it hadn't kept turning, spinning like it always has.* Did you hear what I said, *she says, wrapped in her own shawl of nervousness, and The Kid nods, hoping the sweat doesn't run down his face, gathering at the tip of his cold, cold nose and drip-drip-dripping onto the table in front of him, hoping she doesn't see the growing panic in his eyes, a panic that might have something to do with being in public after so long, but doesn't—it actually has moreso to do with the words* I'm Pregnant *hanging over the table like the sudden appearance of a storm cloud in an otherwise clear sky.*

"Just shut UP," I say, drawing my leg back to give Frank a swift kick for his troubles, and it's only as I aim my boot at what's left of Frank that I realize the back tire has stopped spinning completely; that the front tire is also motionless, buried in a tuffet of roadside grass that hasn't seen a mower blade since early spring; that the squeaking is actually coming from deeper in the ditch, a squeaking that sounds less like a tire needing some grease and more like a hot and pissed-off bundle of orange fur struggling mightily to push its way through ropy waves of ditch grass, out of that snarled heather, past unreliable-ass Frank and right toward me.

"Oh no," I say, my shoulders slumping even more. I look left, up the road toward home. I look right and back toward the failed job interview. No cars coming, or going, nobody to see this idiot standing by the side of the road, talking to himself, nothing and no one now, just me and Frank and what looks to be a bright orange baby racoon.

It squeaks.

"No fucking way."

Another annoyed squeak, longer and squeakier this time. Definitely pissed off.

"Absolutely not. I just... I'm not..."

I lean over and yank Frank out of the ditch. I don't have words, not any that would offer up a valid excuse, anyway. And I begin walking home. Slightly limping. Frank rolling along beside me, limping in his own way. Leaving the scuffed dirt and ditch and tuft of thick grass and its tiny occupant right there, just so, as the words *FAST-PACED* and *TEAM-ORIENTED* and *I'M PREGNANT* and *EXCELLENT FOOD* and *GREAT CUSTOMER SERVICE* and *I'M PREGNANT* and CLEAN EVIORNMENT, EVIORNMENT, EVIORNMENT make hollow, defeated echoes in the otherwise silent chamber of my head.

CHAPTER TWO

I'm sweating heavy by the time I roll Frank up the driveway. The remnants of last night's coolness have all but faded, evaporating into the sky beneath the midmorning sun's ever-present glare. I dump the bike in front of the fence separating the backyard from the front, unlocking the back door with a beat-up key and a couple *cmon-dammit* jiggles, and I go inside, slamming the door shut behind me. There's a foyer of sorts, with a small set of stairs leading up into the house itself and a larger (if crookeder) set of stairs that goes beneath the house to the basement, where it's low and cool and damp, and smells that way, like the windows have been left open too many times, too much outsideness inside. The beams down there, they're just low enough to make a body hunch his shoulders and dip his head a little, lest a body knock himself silly on one of those beams, carrying his head all high and mighty like that. And there's a couple mildew-encrusted windows, a massive heating unit that I really hope works in a couple months, a small nook with a couple workbenches upon which are scattered the meager beginnings of a tool collection, some stuff for the yard, rakes and shears and a snow shovel, two, three snow shovels; and some boxes and other shit piled just to the right of the crooked stairs, what looks to be a makeshift cat tree, if I'm remembering correctly, and a pet bed of sorts. And not much else, assuming I *am* remembering correctly, with corners that've only ever seen the occasional beam of evening sun pouring through spots on the mildewed window facing directly west, burnished gold the color of a squeezed oranges, warm yellowy-orangey-reds like fall, like a middle-school fight in mid-October, like nursing a bloody nose beneath a mass of half-naked branches without crying, the first time you've ever gotten hurt, like really hurt, and not cried. The washer and dryer are down there, which is basically the only reason I ever go to the basement. And there's a dead mouse stuck to the floor right there in front of them, placed very inconveniently, like right where I need to step when I'm switching the laundry over, close enough to the mouse's empty eye sockets and gaping maw and *the way their bodies are pinned against the seats, like they'd been punched too many times to ever get up, and their heads, or pieces of them, and flames licking at them hungrily, all of them Dead with a capital D, all of them wilting against each other like melted candles, all of them—*

I take the stairs going up in a bound, and I start opening windows, three in the living room, two in the empty front bedroom, two in the back bedroom, and one in the bathroom, which only opens about halfway. Then back to the kitchen, two windows in there, and I open the fridge door, hopefully perusing the almost-bare interior. I'm down to my last loaf of bread. There's a few pieces of lunch meat left, some mustard, and exactly one piece of the cheapest cheese I could find. So it's eat now or eat later, can't have both, and there's no telling when I'll be able to buy more.

Days?

Weeks?

How long until I find a job? Any job?

"Who fucking knows." I scoop the refrigerator's meager offering into my arms and slam the door, trying to ignore the complete absence of alcohol within, which was the *real* reason I'd opened the fridge in the first place. And I stand at the counter, just next to the sink, slapping a sandwich together with a rather unhungry lack of haste, doing it moreso for the sake of doing it than anything else, and if the end result is any indication, it's probably a good thing Subway hadn't hired me to art their sandwiches after all.

I stare out the window, aiming my gaze directly west, because if a young man cannot go west, as young men are so wont to do, then staring in a general westwardly direction is, presumably, the next best thing.

Maybe I should have grabbed that kitten. Karma doesn't have an expiration date. But what would I've even done with it, can't feed the poor bastard, can barely feed myself, JESUS. I take a rather belabored bite out of the sandwich. It tastes like sawdust slathered in mustard, and I battle the overwhelming urge I have to toss it in the trash. *And besides, me and cats, we've got a history—we go way back like the seats in a Cadillac. And besides* that, *I don't have time to take care of a kitten, I mean, I barely have time to take care of* myself.

The latter wasn't entirely true. I'd had nothing *but* time on my hands over the past several months. I'd come across this tiny house by way of a friend's friend shortly after being released from prison, and it'd been perfect, for what I needed anyway: a place to stay while I looked for a job and tried to finish the book I've been writing for the past three years. The owner of the house, she'd called it Getting Back On Your Feet, and the implication was that eventually, I'd get a job, a *real* one, and I'd start paying rent like a decent, upstanding member of society, because this is what Getting Back On Your Feet entails, that you find gainful employment and start making money to give to other people.

But Getting Back On My Feet had taken longer than expected. Writing in the early morning, then hunting for jobs, checking Craigslist first, then riding Frank through the small town just up the road and dropping my resume at various places and filling out applications, making sure to check *yes* next the question asking if I've ever been convicted of a felony, and this is the way things went for a while, just same shit, different day, over and over again, and never getting a call back, and I mean, me-oh-my, I wonder why. But telling myself that things were gonna change. That they *had* to. That I'd find a job eventually. And finish the book. That I wouldn't be forever stuck borrowing money from Emily, my best friend since high school, just to feed myself. That I wouldn't continue to lie to myself about the real reason I had to keep borrowing money, which was to support a drinking habit that'd long since become more than a *habit.*

I wonder if I have enough change to maybe get just a couple. Maybe. With the cans. I check the bag of empty beer cans beneath the sink, taking another reluctant bite of sandwich. Looks to be a dollar's worth. *Definitely maybe.*

And speaking of maybes... maybe I should've grabbed that kitten...

My phone buzzes against my leg. I'm supposed to be Getting Back On My Feet, not playing Captain Save-A-Kitty. I take another bite of the sandwich, switching hands before digging it out of my pocket. It's the aforementioned Emily, and so I answer.

"Well, well, well. Speak of the devil and she shall appear."

"Hey, what's up?" She says, her voice crackling through the speakers of my shitty phone like a handful of crushed pretzels.

"Not shit, just got back from that job interview."

"The one for the waitress?"

I smile dryly. "You're so funny."

"Waiter? Whenever I say waiter it makes me think of some upscale place, though," she says. "Doesn't feel right."

"Upscale? Well, waitress is very gender specific, I feel like."

"How about *server*?"

"Server, sure. But this interview was the one for sandwich artistry."

"Was it only that one? I thought you had a couple job interviews."

"Nope, just the one. Although I did apply for two. But apparently nobody wants a convicted felon serving their food."

"I don't think people care who serves their food, to be honest."

"I'm relatively certain that our society has tailored us to feel most comfortable receiving our food from college girls."

"The ones going to school for psychology," she says, laughing.

"No, cosmetology."

"Major in psychology with a minor in—"

"Minor in cosmetology. Cut your hair *and* cut to the root of all your problems."

"At the same damn time."

"Right."

"So the job interview?"

"Yeah." I think about taking another bite of this dry fare, and decide against it, choosing instead to Kobe it into the crooked trashcan in the corner. "Didn't get it."

"Oh. You got the uh—"

"Weak handshake. Cold and clammy, like shaking hands with a fish. And the classic *we'll be in touch*."

"Okay, so, no big deal," she says. I can almost hear her squaring her shoulders. "I mean, fuck 'em. You'll find something. Do you have any other applications in?"

"Putting more in today. But I mean, *fuck 'em, you'll find something*— that's losing its luster. Especially since the baby is due in like six weeks."

"Babies don't need shit, man, ask anybody. Jessica will probably have a baby shower. Or you could have a diaper party. Your friends bring a case of diapers and a case of beer each. It's supposed to be this big party, everybody getting drunk, everybody trying on diapers and shit."

"This doesn't seem like something that happens."

"It's a thing. You should do it. I'd come, me and Wes would."

"Grand total of three people at this diaper party of yours."

"Well uh...I forgot you don't have any other friends."

"Anyway," I say. "We digress. So, listen, I'm riding my bike back from—"

"It still works? The bike? I would've thought it'd taken a shit by now."

"Well, it did take a shit, on the way back, actually." I tell her what happened, being sure to exclude the part where I ate complete shit into the ditch.

"Wait, you found *what*?" Her voice raises a couple excited octaves. "Is it cat or a kitten? What color is it? Did somebody leave it? Fucking assholes, I bet it's starving. Are you feeding it? What does it look like, can you send me a picture?"

I cringe a little bit. "You know, your vagina really shows whenever somebody mentions kittens."

"So it *is* a kitten! *Is it fucking CUTE?* And see, the day wasn't all bad. You found a friend."

I snort. "A friend?"

"Well, my cats are dicks. But not all of them are. It'll probably be grateful you saved it. Is it a boy or a girl? How big is it?"

"Listen. I would answer all of those questions. But...I didn't bring it with me."

"Wait... *what*? *YOU LEFT IT?*"

"Yeah, I left it, what am I supposed to do? Put it in my fucking pocket?"

"Hold on. *WAIT.* Let me get this straight. Someone hates cute and furry things, so they dumped this kitten—"

"Maybe they just hate the responsibility associated."

"WAIT, I said. So some dumbass dumped this cute-ass kitten, and you compounded their dumbassery by being an even bigger dumbass and leaving it there."

"And I don't have the best history with cats—"

"In the ditch."

"Me and cats go way back, okay—"

"By itself."

"..."

"A kitten."

"I can't afford to take care of a cat, Emily."

"Yeah, I'm sure it's so much better off in the fucking ditch. I'm sure it's just having a fucking blast out there." She's steaming.

"It's supposed to be hotter than a six-chick porn flick today, now you mention it," I say, but the joke falls flat. "And all of this is actually really weird, because I'm pretty sure there's a fucking cat tree in the basement."

"See? It's a SIGN."

"It's a coincidence."

"Go get it. Now."

"I will do no such thing."

"I hate you so much right now."

"I know. Get in line." A weary sarcasm.

"*You* deserve to be left in a ditch."

"On that note," I say, leaving the implication dangling in mid-air.

"Go get that kitten, you dick."

"Goodbye, Emily."

"*GO GET THAT POOR LITTLE—*"

CHAPTER THREE

The Kid and cats go waaaay back, like the seats in a Cadillac, i.e. The Kid's like nine or something, and he's at the county fair, having fun for once, feeling accepted and part of the family for once. And isn't it strange? He's riding rides and sampling funnel cake and inhaling the scent of the fairway, the salty and sweet and oily smell of summer's end, deep into the night, until like ten or eleven, when the lanes separating the rides and vendors and games and funhouses and pig races and live music completely empty, leaving behind nothing but sticky refuse and trampled grass. The grass will rise again, in a few weeks, tall and straight and proud, and it will be as if the fair never existed, and never mind how much The Kid thinks about it over the next 20 years, the events of this night, about the fair and going home, the street lights flicking by at a steady pace, lighting up tired faces and sleepy eyes and sticky cheeks, and remembering along the way what awaits when he, The Kid, gets home— that the cat, Bootsie, has left a litter of kittens beneath his bed, tucked away in the farthest corner, blanketed in darkness and warmth, hidden from sight. Because, you know, Bootsie's an outside cat and she needs to have her fucking kittens outside, and don't be letting her through your window like I know you do sometimes, because I don't want those things in my fucking house, and et cetera.

But the cat had been yowling outside his bedroom window for like an hour last night, keeping The Kid awake with the song of her people, so he'd eventually let her in, sliding the window open quietly, just enough for the cat jump, cling, and squeeze through. She'd crawled underneath the bed, and although The Kid knew on some level what she was doing under there, he'd accidentally fell asleep anyway. And he'd awoken to a ragged symphony of squeaks, knowing instantly that he was in big trouble, if the cold sinking in his stomach was any indication. He'd rolled out of bed, straight to the floor, lying flat on his belly, and there she was, Bootsie, tending to what looked like a mass of undulating fur. And The Kid had just left her alone, pacing his room and worrying. There's not much he can do, is there, he can't exactly just dump them outside his window and hope for the best. But if the mom finds out about it, if she even suspects, he's gonna be in the deepest doo-doo.

Luckily enough, nobody had come into The Kid's room for the entire *day. His secret was safe. The Kid was safe. For now.*

And but, now he's thinking, trying to remember if he'd shut his bed-room door when they left for the fair, or if he'd left it open in his excitement to be having fun for once, feeling accepted and part of the family for once. Because leaving it open meant that the kittens weren't safe, not without their mama there, whom The Kid had let back outside, per her yowling request. The kittens weren't safe because of the mom's dog, this tiny yappy asshole, spoiled and the apple of the mom's eye and all that. The type that gets Christmas presents, better ones than The Kid. The type of dog that wears clothes, eats the best food, and hates everyone in the family but the mom. Who especially hates The Kid, probably because the dog thinks he's a stranger, given how little The Kid is allowed to leave his room.

He's panicking now. The dog had *shown an interest in his room today. Scratching at the door. Snuffling at the crack beneath. Whining, begging to be let in so he could do whatever it is asshole dogs with no discipline do to newborn kittens. And The Kid is thinking hard,* had *he closed the door? Surely he had. Because the alternative...*

The time passing seems both too fast and too slow, but then they're home, thumping up their potholed driveway, and The Kid doesn't wait, flings the car door open and hurries inside. He goes straight to his room, and before he even gets there, he can see that his door is, in fact, not closed. The Kid's dreading it, but he pushes the door all the way open, doesn't hesitate, and turns on the lights. His heart is pounding too hard, and he's feeling a little sick now, not accepted *and* part of the family *like he had been, riding rides and sampling funnel cake and inhaling the scent of the fairway, the salty and sweet and oily smell of summer's end, and how strange* had *all of it been? It's all fading now, as the fears of what he's been struggling with for the past half-hour, the entire car ride, become actualized. The Kid starts crying, not that he means to, because isn't he too old to be crying? This is more than just some spilled milk though.*

But nobody cares. The mom kind of laughs, even, when she comes to see what it is he's crying about. The Kid doesn't know how or why, but she shrugs the whole thing off, the fact that her asshole dog has dragged two of the kittens from beneath the bed, tearing them into pieces that now litter the floor of The Kid's bedroom. Their mouths gape open in silent screams, their insides stringy and stretched out and, some of it, dangling from the dog's mouth as it comes in behind them, panting and happy and begging to be fucking kicked, *The Kid thinks, begging to be drowned in a fucking* creek, *he thinks, growing angrier by the second. But the mom just kind of chuckles, shrugging and telling The Kid,* Hadn't she said not to let that fucking cat have her kittens in the house, had she not? NOW CLEAN IT UP, *she says, snatching the dog up and cuddling him into her chest, leaving The Kid to do just that. He cries the whole time, but more quietly now, so as to draw less attention to himself; and he goes to bed after the fact, staring at the ceiling for hours, deep into the night, his white-hot hate for the little dog slowly giving way to shame and guilt. Because she was right, wasn't she? All of this was ultimately his fault.* He *was the one who let Bootsie in through his window, knowing how close she was to giving birth. He was the one who had forgotten to shut his door, hadn't he? And* he *was the one crying himself to sleep tonight, folding his pillow around his head to muffle the sound of Bootsie yowling at his window, begging to be let in so she can tend to the rest of her kittens. He can't tell her, but* he *is the reason they exist now only in pieces; that they're no longer in his room; that they're actually on the back porch in a trash can, next to what's left of the mewing mound of fur she'd entrusted to him. All of it unceremonious and uncaring in a way that just feels* strange *to The Kid, stranger than being only nine, and at the county fair, having fun for once, feeling* accepted *and* part of the family *for once, because as time has shown, and will show again and again, there's not much stranger than that.*

    The Kid just can't forget about it, that night, being only nine, and at the county fair, having fun for once, feeling accepted *and* part of the family *for once; but when he thinks about it, the county fair and all of its gloriousness is faded, nearly forgotten, and all he's left with are the very vivid memories of all the mistakes he made leading up to that night, all the things he did wrong. How he had failed Bootsie, how he was the*

reason those kittens had died such a gruesome death. Sometimes, late-late at night, he finds himself imagining what it must have sounded like, their little screams, and it makes him sick, punches him in the stomach with a strong bile fist, drags him down, deep-deep-deep into a darkness so dark; and he sticks, gets stuck down there, deep in his head, and this is where The Kid finds his solutions, various fixes for what ails him. So while he's never actually tried to kill himself before today, he's certainly thought about it, considered it in the very vaguest sense of what it means to kill oneself, to commit suicide, a voluntary kicking of the fucking bucket or whatever.

In his head, there's no pain or suffering or anything associated with the aforementioned suicidal thoughts. No, these are things The Kid associates with being alive. When he does think about killing himself, it manifests as a drifting off to sleep, soft and slow and unassuming and relieving; and in his head, these ideas justify their existence by telling The Kid that killing himself is just a sort of recharging session before Everything That Comes After.

But there's a natural progression that leads The Kid here. Seminatural. For instance, he'd tried Running Away *first, hadn't he? And the details concerning that particular failed mission were pretty cut and dried: He'd packed all of the fucks he had left to give, hoisted that empty sack up over his shoulder, and he'd just, you know,* Run Away. *But, as anyone who's ever* Run Away *before knows, there's not much running associated with* Running Away. *Lots of creeping. Some skulking. Because when you* Run Away, *the goal is to leave without anyone noticing, and the merest of interactions with someone could derail the whole fucking thing. So he'd just kinda creeped around, waiting for an opening big enough for him to fit through unnoticed, and then he'd just sorta skulked away—the sound of everything around him so quiet; the whispering of Georgia grass brushing against high socks; the distant hush-hush of cars trundling down rain-slick road; the murmuring of a faraway train approaching, or maybe going away; and it was as if the quietness, all of the whispering and hushing and murmuring, was predicated on the assumption that the moms or somebody would stick their head out the back door and ask him where exactly the fuck he thought he was going, where the fuck he was creeping and skulking off to.*

Only they hadn't. And it was only after a while, once he'd gotten out of sight, that he began to actually run.

It had been short-lived, the whole ordeal. He'd burned through the initial excitement of it all pretty quick, and then he just walked for a while, albeit quickly, weighing his scant options, thinking maybe he'd see what the trainyard had to offer. If there's one thing Waycross, Georgia has, it's trains and trainyards; and he'd be good as gold, wouldn't he, as long as hopping a train *proved to be as easy he thought it might.*

The Kid hadn't made it to the trainyard, though. Having no idea where it was had played a vital part. He knows where the corner store is, a little Flash Foods down the way a bit. There are a couple fields to cut across and a dirt road to follow, but then you're there. Other than that tiny bit of information, he'd just been winging it, because living life behind a chain-locked door leaves one with little in the way of a serviceable compass. So what had started as creeping and skulking, and then some actual running and fast walking, had turned into more of a meandering, which is what he'd been doing along the side of some random, poorly paved road when a cop car pulled up, slowing to a stop just in front of him.

Hey kid, *the cop said, stepping out of the car, hooking his thumbs in his belt in a way that was maybe meant to put The Kid at ease, but didn't.* What's your name?

Jason?

He'd said it like a question, as if he wasn't sure, and later, after the cop had guided him gently into the backseat of his patrol car and driven him home and turned him over to his parents; after his stepdad had beaten the urge to Run Away *out of The Kid with kicks in the ass and ringing swats to the head and at least one punch in the stomach, maybe two; and after he'd been lectured by the mom, who stood while he sat on the edge of his bed, who eyed him like he was a fucking bug or something, who smoked Misty Light 100s and called down the narrow hallway for another cup of coffee, the rim of which she blemished with cheap lipstick the color of bubblegum-flavored Dum Dums; only after all of that did The Kid wonder why in the fuck he hadn't at least* tried *to lie to the damn cop.*

And he saw it for what it was, then, after that. The options afforded to him were few; and that if he truly wanted to be rid of the pre–Hogwarts Harry Potterish lifestyle with which he was afflicted, the only real and true and good-golly-gosh-guaranteed option was to kill himself.

CHAPTER FOUR

I'm in the kitchen, just kinda standing there, staring out the window, procrastinating. The grass in the backyard needs a trim. There are some branches that need to be picked up, a couple of the bigger ones having been wrenched from the trees and tossed down within frightening proximity to the house itself, and—

Some dumbass dumped this cute-ass kitten, and you compounded their dumbassery by being an even bigger dumbass.

And the fence line wouldn't turn its nose up at a taste of the weed-eater, would it, not from the looks of it. I could certainly take care of it, and there's maybe an afternoon's worth of work right there. It's not *paid* work, just something to take my mind off the fact that I'm no closer to finding *paid* work than I was when I left this morning.

I'm sure it's so much better off in the fucking ditch, Jason.

And if that doesn't tickle my fancy, there are certainly other things to do, like, I dunno, maybe writing? I could write. The book's not finishing itself, is it, and even if one can't create, one can edit, or so those who have actually managed to turn their writing into a living wage would have one believe. And just never mind the crippling self-doubt that comes with the territory, or the gray and tasteless quality the words don upon a second glance, a reread that only leads to a depression that worsens and deepens with every word and paragraph and page read, until all that's left is a big fuck-it, a trip to the corner store, tall boys purchased with pocket change accrued from the recycling of past tall boys, and an early bed time, which is usually less about how tired I am, or might be, and moreso about how much I've consumed, typically more than the recommended dosage in less than the recommended time.

GO GET THAT POOR LITTLE—

"FUCK!"

I spin away from the counter and stomp downstairs. There's a pile of boxes just to the right of the stairs, stacked haphazardly next to the makeshift cat tree that had apparently been left behind from the last time somebody rented this place, and all of them are too big for the task at hand, the boxes—just big enough to be really awkward. I grab one that doesn't look too bad and tip it upside down.

It's a bunch of cat stuff. A bed. What looks like some well-worn toys, little mice and whatnot. And an expired bottle of something, dewormer maybe.

See? It's a SIGN.

"OKAY, SHUT UP, I'M GOING!" I say, kicking one of the other boxes for good measure, hyperextending my knee for good measure. "SONOFABITCH!"

And I stomp back up the stairs, cursing and sweating now. Limping even more now. And I stomp some more, or rather, I gimp some more, out of the house, slamming the door as if there's anyone to see me do it, and I head off down the road in the direction from whence I'd just come, pressured by the guilt I feel, a rancid and acidic guilt chewing away at the dry lump in my stomach, a sour taste in my heart lending clarity to the idea in my head—

Aren't you tired of being the bad guy?

Black widows. Genus Latrodectus. *Found throughout much of the world. Most commonly* L mactans *in North America. Also,* L hesperus *and* L curacaviensis *and* L geometricus, *depending on where you are exactly. In the Southeastern part of the US, this is where The Kid lives, the* L curacaviensis *can be found in trees and shrubs and* L mactans *can be found on the ground quite easily. The Kid's seen them before, couple places outside, nestled away in their webs, perhaps sleeping, perhaps not. Do spiders sleep? The Kid hasn't been able to find much on a spider's sleep cycle in his 1976 World Book Encyclopedia, but he's found out tons more, enough to go off of. Such as, for instance: what they look like, fat and black and sporting a deeply red hourglass on their underside. Such as, for instance: that finding a male black widow is nearly impossible, what with the violent nature of their mates, because they're killed and eaten after mating, the males are. Such as, for instance: that the bite of*

a black widow can bring on a bevy of horrifying symptoms, muscle pains and vomiting and difficulty breathing. Such as, for instance: that the bite can be fatal to the elderly and small children. And The Kid doesn't know if he's quite small enough to qualify as a small child, but there's only one way to find out.

It's hot. Too hot. It's always too hot in Georgia, even when it's cold. It's even hotter where he is, The Kid, standing in his stepdad's shed in the backyard, this hulking metallic beast, this mound of rusted metal sup-ported by rotting wood and not much else. A good summer storm might take it down, knocking it flat and crushing The Kid beneath it, were one to make an appearance on this dreadfully hot summer day. Storms are known to do that down here, starting as a few white clouds on the horizon, and then progressing rather quickly into something else, the clouds swelling and pulsating and turning a not-so-clean sort of white, and then gray, and then a horrible grayish black, as the distant crack of struck lightning gets closer and closer. The Kid has learned quite a lot about these storms via his trusty encyclopedia. Such as, for instance: that counting the seconds between the flash of lightning and the accompanying crash of thunder and then dividing by five will tell you how far away the storm is. Such as, for instance: that being closer to the storm means more of a clap-boom-rumble than a rumble-boom-clap. Such as, for instance: that while The Kid has the proverbial one-in-a-million chance of being taken out by a bolt of lightning, the actual odds are more like 1 in 160,000. Still not good enough odds for The Kid. Not on this day....

But so, if you think it's hot outside, you should feel the inside of this shed, stand in The Kid's shoes for a minute. There's a thin layer of constant perspiration on your skin when you live down here, not much gets rid of it outside of a hardworking AC unit, but The Kid's not merely perspiring. He feels positively drenched, from his too-big shirt to his too-small pants. He rakes his hand back through his hair, pushing a hot tumbleweed back off his forehead, but it just flops back into place. The floor of the shed is just dirt, dry and sandy in some parts, damp and rotting in others, and it boggles The Kid's mind to think of all that lies beneath, cutworms and green June beetles and mole crickets and white grubs and wireworms and various what's-its and et cetera, all of them oblivious to The Kid and his mission; and the smell of the place is almost too much, wet rust and dried grease and splintering wood and aerated metal. The walls are covered with random gardening tools, shovels and rakes and shears and posthole diggers, and they leer at The Kid quite menacingly, maybe offering their services, like hey kid, don't you need a helping hand with all of this? *And beneath the ugly tools and their shadows, there's a stack of rotting shingles to the left, another to the right, and a long shelf made out of even more rotting wood and covered in various screws and bolts and roofing tacks and rusted screwdrivers and drill bits and dirty hammers, a scattering of discarded things. It's a packrat's wet dream.*

You should really clean this place up, *he whispers, and jumps a little at the sound of his own voice. The Kid's not supposed to be in here, in the shed, or so he's been told. But if you're looking for bugs, if you're looking for spiders, this is the place to be, and The Kid knows this because he's been in here countless times, always careful to lift a little on the door so it doesn't drag along the ground as he pulls, making enough god-awful noise to wake the frickin dead, to notify others of the current goings-on, and then he squeezes right in there, easy-peasy. And if he turns to his immediate left, there between the shingles and the wall, there's a dusty, cobwebbed collection of shovels, maybe four or five of them, all of them broken and dull and basically useless unless you're looking for what The Kid's looking for, which is to say—*

Black widows. Genus Latrodectus. *Found throughout much of the world. Found throughout much of the shed, actually, in it and atop it and behind it and beneath it. The Kid's had his eye on one in particular, this one here, rather large and shiny, as far as black widows go, and he's been in here to check on her several times over the past week. Sometimes he hopes she's still there and sometimes he hopes otherwise, hopes maybe the collection of crappy shovels has fallen over somehow, taking the spider and her web with it to the ground, and then skit-skit-skitter, she'd be gone, and The Kid would take that to mean the whole thing's just not meant to be. Because of course there's a part of him that doesn't wanna do it, of course there is. One's desire to commit suicide isn't usually about not wanting to* live, *per say. It's moreso about not wanting to live like* this, *The Kid thinks, like spending every day in this house with these people, his parents and siblings, continuing to exist in spite of every attempt on their part to make it seem like he doesn't, in spite of this growing desire The Kid feels to just give in, one last fuck-it, a desire that grows with every beating and derisive comment they send his way, grows so much that The Kid can't ignore it anymore, he can't fucking stand it anymore; and so he'd picked a day, maybe six days out, a Friday, and he'd checked on her every one of those six days, creeping/skulking into the shed, slipping quietly through the sweltering darkness to the pile of broken shovels in the corner, and she'd been there every single time, same spot, almost as if she hadn't moved an inch, almost as if she was there for only one reason. And it was no different today, and TGIF, because there she was, there she is, right where she had been, waiting for The Kid to gather the guts to grab her and put her on his wrist, something he's pictured countless times. He can almost feel her bite pricking him. He pictures the venom being carried up his arm to his heart, stopping it mid-beat, pictures them coming to his room in the morning and finding his cold and lifeless body just lying there, pictures them burying The Kid and shedding a few tears maybe, and pictures them actually giving a fuck about him, about The Kid, because if there's anything that'll make you shed some tears in spite of yourself, it's a dead kid, he thinks. Who knows, maybe they'd love me if I was dead, The Kid thinks.*

He gathers the guts and reaches for the web, pushing past the tangled mass of sticky threads and grabbing the upside-down spider by one of her legs. He's nervous, his hands shaking, and he can feel her body curling up toward his finger, dangling there like a rancid grape, her seven other legs wrapping around the tip and dangling there cancerously, her maw shining and sticky and flexing, and he can't help it, he drops her, something primal inside him shying away from contact with this venomous creature. She hits the dirt with a small puff, and that's it, The Kid thinks, there went his chance, she's gonna skitter off beneath something and that will be it; but she doesn't, just curls up there in the dirt, playing dead and waiting for The Kid's next move. He hurries for something to scoop her up, looking for a little sliver of wood, a stick or something, but she doesn't respond to his eventual poking and prodding. There's an anxiety growing in The Kid's chest now, throbbing in his stomach like a swung hammer,

43

and right on cue, he hears the back door to the house open.

GAYSON!

Which is what his stepdad calls him when he's in a good mood, because The Kid likes reading and writing and only faggots are into that kind of shit, don't you know?

HEY GAYSON!

The Kid can hear the exasperation in his stepdad's voice, the good mood deteriorating swiftly, because who is this little faggy kid to make him call out twice? The Kid's gonna get it now, he can already feel the ringing slaps raining down on him, and it's now or never, isn't it, so he just goes for it, grabs the spider by one of her legs again and gets a good hold on it this time, and before he can talk himself out of it, he drops her on the underside of his left wrist.

She uncurls her legs, stretching them out.

The Kid applies a little pressure, just enough to provoke a response.

And she strikes, once.

And then again.

And again, several times in quick succession, tiny pinpricks dotting The Kid's wrist, and except for a couple mild winces, that's it, it's over before it began nearly, and he takes her by one of her legs once more, dropping her gently back into her web.

Thank you, *he whispers, feeling dumb, but truly meaning it. There's a relief flooding him, rushing through his veins and washing away his anxiety, his fear and sadness, his helplessness too; because he is in control for what feels like the very first time in his entire life.*

The door is pulled open then, the bottom of it screaming along the ground, because what the fuck are you doing in here, *and The Kid jumps, hurries for one of the broken shovels, pulling it from the stack and holding it up.*

Grabbing a shovel, *he says, and a smile rebels across the bottom of his face. It'll earn him a couple extra slaps, but it feels worth it.*

Cmon, get the fuck outta here, *he says, stepping to the side so The Kid can walk past him. The Kid doesn't even flinch as his stepdad raises his hand, he takes the slap like a man might, and although it's a pretty hard smack, it's not enough to wipe the smile off The Kid's face.* The fuck are you smiling at?

Nothing, *The Kid says, shrugging, smiling even more. He absorbs another couple slaps with an eerie calm, ignoring the pain and concentrating on the prickling warmth that's begun to throb on the underside of his left wrist. An impromptu storm is gathering on the horizon.* Nothing at all.

The pain is magnificent. It feels like fall. The smell of burning wood. The silent drift of falling leaves, the crisp days, and apples. Big, bright red apples. It means fat, orange pumpkins and as many pecans as will fit into the makeshift basket of your shirt. Fall means the end of summer. With the end of summer go the days at the beach, the deep tans and popsicles. No one eats popsicles in the fall. The days grow shorter, the sun reluctant to rise and quick to set, the rays vanishing over the horizon in a rosy glow that reminds one of kissed cheeks and pocketed hands. It gets dark quick, and that's the thing to remember about the fall. The darkness. *He's lying in bed, The Kid is, half in and half out, fading and coming back. His entire arm has gone cold, swelling at the wrist and climbing slowly, creeping toward his heart like a predator on the hunt. He feels all cold, then all hot, and the urge to scream out in pain is quelled only by the fact that he can't scream, can't make any noise outside of a few pitiful squeaks.*

With the darkness comes the nightmares. They are few and far between during the summer, and if he tries hard enough, he can keep them at bay for the most part. For his own sake, he tells himself that it's something that he is doing, something different, and that he finally has it under control. They don't come for a week, sometimes two or three even, and he forgets. He forgets just enough to be surprised when they come for him in the fall, the fading fingers of summer loosening, the days shorter and the nights longer. They come for him in the dark. They are the reason he hates the dark. The reason he fears it. *And he feels sick, not sick like he ate something bad, not sick like he's got the flu or something, but* sick, *really and truly* sick. *He feels like he's going to vomit, and the pain in his stomach is of another world, a much harsher world, and he slowly begins to feel, as is common in situations like this, like maybe living wasn't so bad after all.* As the light fades on another day, he drifts, sliding deeply into a semiconscious state in which he is aware of the things going on around him, as well as the things going on inside him. It starts with a rush—faint, distant. It sounds like running water and it is pleasant, lulling him into an even deeper state of sleep. As it grows, as the sound picks up, he realizes it is not the mild trickle of water in a nearby stream, into which one might—if he were inclined—toss a line and come away with a fat, wriggling trout; nor is it a river, wild and dangerous, rough and beautiful. It is not a waterfall, breathtaking to behold, breaking flashing beams of sunlight into rainbow-colored prisms; nor an ocean, deep and dreadful at its core, mild and pleasant at its edges. It is not water at all, he realizes, as it grows louder and louder in his ears. It is wind. Wild gusts of ferocious wind that blind, deafen, mute.

Sometimes, he can fight it. He struggles to pull himself from the quicksand that is sleep, willing himself to wake up, willing himself to move. Sometimes he prevails and bolts awake, the bed creaking in protest as he sits up, sweating and shivering, but safe. Other times, he fails. When this happens, when he cannot pull himself back, no matter how hard he tries, he falls into the deepest pits of sleep, where nightmares are made in the dark, where they are kept in that sable abyss, far from the world of the living. He has come for just a visit, but it is not all too certain he will leave. *But there's no going back now, he's made his bed and now he must lie in it, painful writhing as an aside, copious amounts of cold sweat as an aside.* A giggle. Just one to start us off, and not a pleasant one. The giggle is the final sign that he is here to stay, for better or worse. Usually for worse. It is an evil laugh, one made at the expense of others. It is sharp and ugly. It is black. Another joins in, as if sharing in the joke. Another. One more. No, several more. There are, within moments, hundreds, thousands of countless dark titters. They wash over him in waves. He is on an empty stage and can see nothing. It is cold and the wind picks up, meshing with the laughter, those goblins that giggle and chitter through sharp teeth and bladed tongues, goblins of the night, and they know he is here. *He can't breathe, The Kid can't fucking* breathe. *Each drawn breath is as if pulled from the depths of an abandoned well.* As the wind roars in his ears, chilling like no wind had ever chilled, ripping and tearing at exposed flesh, blending with the chittering demons effortlessly, he's forced to his knees. *And he can't move his fucking legs, he can't move anything.* And the chatter of the goblins fills his ears, peels back his eyelids and scrapes at his eyes like a shower of powdered glass, infiltrates his head and bounces off the inside like chucked grenades, and he can feel himself being compressed downward, and inward, as if a giant hand is reaching down to press him into a ball, and he can feel his jaws being pried open, and he clenches them closed, because if they get his mouth open, he's gonna fucking drown, but then they do, and *The Kid tries to call out, tries to raise his voice to an octave that will be heard, that will bring someone, anyone, to his side, because this wasn't the way he'd pictured it, kicking the fucking bucket, this isn't falling asleep forever and just like drifting away or something. It's pain and horror and fear. It's dark back there behind the veil, an infinite darkness, The Kid can feel it, and he begins to scream then,* but only in the dream, and not because he needs to, but because he must, he must scream, he must do something to expel the blackness filling his mouth and his throat, to drown out the sound of the wind filling his ears, the sound of goblins chattering and giggling, so he screams and he screams and he screams, but those shrill and terrified notes will never reach the edges of the black abyss in which he is trapped, no matter how much he screams—*wake up, wake up, WAKE UP*—no matter how much he tries to leave this place, this dark, this evil fucking place, because *The Kid's like three beers in, well, three beers and how many ever—*

It's a long walk back to where I'd seen the kitten, seemingly longer than it had taken to pick up my bike and roll the bastard home. Long enough that I start to wonder if maybe I'd passed the spot. Or maybe somebody had come along after me and taken the kitten, wouldn't that be glorious, and I'd leave my too-big box on the side of the road, because fuck it, and I'd be free of the responsibility, free to head back home and shower off the sweat and count my pocket change and my recyclables and maybe, just maybe, free to take whatever coinage I could muster and head to the store for an ice-cold beer.

I'm actually smiling a little, there's a little pep in my step now, and I'm on the verge of giving up and heading back when I hear several annoyed squeaks. I see the scuffed dirt and the tuft of thick grass and the tiny occupant within, and my smile melts away, my shoulders resume their dejected slump, and I drop the box and step down into the ditch, reaching for it, the orange blotch of fur, intent on just doing it and getting it fucking over with, when the thing launches itself at my proffered hand.

"Oh shit!" I say, surprised, and I yank my hand away. It's hissing and spitting like a ball of electricity, orange hair sticking up this way and that, and I get my first good look at the kitten, at the giant *M* marking on its forehead, the tiny ringed tail sticking out aggressively, glaring eyes and prickly white whiskers and tiny needles in its mouth, on its paws. It looks pissed off, and bat-shit crazy to boot. "What am I even thinking...."

But I'm here, and there's nothing to it but to do it, so I reach for the kitten again, over its darting maw to the back of its neck, where I snag a pinch of skin. I pull it away from the tuft of grass, and it's wriggling like a caught fish, mouth kinda slack now; but the eyes are still hot and angry, glaring at me, and I drop it in the box before something happens that makes me change my mind again.

"There," and I pull the cardboard flaps this way and that, fashioning them into a top of sorts. I expect to feel a sense of accomplishment or something, having lent myself to a good cause, but I don't. What I feel is hot and annoyed and thirsty, not for water, but so thirsty, a feeling intensifying by the moment. I grab the box, so much more awkward with the kitten's weight shifting all around in there, and I climb the ditch, up to the road, and I'm mentally preparing myself for the long walk back when

I hear another squeaking coming from down in the ditch.

"What in the—"

I turn and peer down into the ditch, past the scuffed dirt and trampled grass. There's another patch of orange fur, this one a little deeper into the ditch than the first had been. I put the box down and rip the cardboard flaps open, and I look inside the box: orange kitten. And I look back down into the ditch: again, orange kitten.

"FUCK!"

I aim a few more choice swear words into the now cloudless sky. The sun has chased off even the faintest memories of the morning's cool start. A passing car meeps. The kitten in the box squeaks. So does the other, which I can only assume is a sibling of sorts.

I hurl one more *fuckingMOTHER* into the atmosphere, willing it in Emily's general direction.

And I step down into the ditch once more.

CHAPTER FIVE

*B*ut *nothing changes after The Kid's suicide attempt. No one knows, no one ever finds out about The Kid's dangerously close brush with death, and so he's not surprised when things stay exactly the damn same. Except for the nightmares, of course, the* night goblins*. The Kid's got the nastiest case of the night goblins as you've ever seen, and they stick with him, coming for him when things get especially dark, waking The Kid up in the dead of night and keeping him that way usually, up until the sun rises, thusly driving the goblins back into the blackest cave in the deepest part of The Kid's mind, where they reside.*

Until the next time. Because there's always a next time.

Years pass. The Kid is 10 or 11. Now he's 12. Now 13. He stays in his room every second of the time he's not out working for his stepdad's new roofing company—for no wages, mind you. He's 14 now. He's 15. But eventually, working for free just isn't cutting it, and they pull The Kid from school so he can work full-time—for no wages, mind you—and he's almost 16 when things finally change. Because they've had enough of The Kid working his ass off for free, enough of him staying locked in his room, wondering if they're going to remember to slide dinner under his door (lord knows he doesn't have the courage to remind them). Or maybe they start to see a spark in his eyes when they're hitting him, when they're denigrating him, a rebel spark that says The Kid's about had enough himself, that says The Kid is starting to think very seriously about swinging back. But whatever the reason, they've just had enough of him, just him*, and enough is enough already, and they kick him out, packing what shit he does have into a backpack and handing him a bus ticket to* Michigan*, of all places, where the mom says he will find his* real dad*, of all things. Because when things change, boy, do they change.*

Now he's going on 17, and meeting his real dad *has turned into living with his* real dad*, but The Kid doesn't know this fucking guy from Adam, and vice versa. They're strangers. His* real dad *shows him pictures of The Kid from way back when—a time when The Kid was happy, it appears, the depicted smiles are contagious—and he calls it* Before Your Mom Took You*, and The Kid doesn't ask his* real dad *why he never came looking for him because he doesn't want to hear the answer. Because it doesn't matter anymore. Because things have changed. The Kid is doing so many things* *for the first time that he can't keep track. He's back in school, which is weird, and he has friends, real friends, which is even weirder, and he's got a real girlfriend too, even weirder still! He forgoes his schoolwork in the process, something he considers a necessary casualty, and he just goes with it, lets life take hold of him and do with him what it will. His past life is just that, the past, and he moves toward the future with gusto, trying his best to ignore the fact that he's not really running toward anything, that all he's actually doing is* Running Away *again. But no matter how much he runs, how much he ignores it all, there's always the night goblins there to remind him, coming for him when things get especially dark, waking* The Kid *up in the dead of night, and keeping him that way usually.*

And he loses himself in the process. Never having been afforded the opportunity, he has no idea who he is in the grand scheme of things. Perhaps this is just the way of things when it comes to teenagers, doing stupid shit and making poor choices for the fuck of it. The Kid isn't familiar with real-world concepts, real-world consequences, and his actions reflect the same. He does things on a whim, doesn't put much thought into how his actions might affect the people around him, and so this is how he finds himself standing in midnight shadows with his new best friend, Emily, shaking a can of red paint, his heart thumping in his ears as he sprays CLASS OF '06 *in big red letters across the school's brick face.*

Why are you writing that, *Emily says, breathless from the feloniousness of it all.* We're not seniors.

I know that, *The Kid says, smirking.* So we'll be the last people they'd ever suspect, no?

Her eyes widen, shining like wet marbles in the dark, and she laughs, but covers it up quickly, lest they be found. How about, I can do something like.... Go Seniors.... or something....

Perfect, *he says, grinning.* Now be quiet, somebody's gonna hear us.

None of it makes as much sense as The Kid's trying to portray. It's trouble for the sake of trouble. It's inconsiderate and stupid, but he can't stop. There's a nasty thrill running through him. His insides feel electric. He mistakes his feelings of anxiety for excitement, and it drives him.

They spray-paint the brick facing, the doors, a couple of new school buses in the parking lot, things like the aforementioned CLASS OF 2006 *and* GO SENIORS, *at least one* CASEVILLE ROCKS, *and several hastily painted '06s adorn the clear, shining surface of the new buses' windows. Then they run away—because The Kid just can't seem to stop* Running Away, *can he—and they forgo the gently lit streets in favor of cutting across dark yards, even hopping a fence at one point, and they make it back to Emily's house just down the street, eyes wide and grins plastered and hair pushed back from running so fast; and what's done is done, and they laugh themselves breathless and tell each other it was just a prank, a harmless joke, and that's not even the kicker folks, because don't look now, it looks like they might just get away with it!*

Or so they think…

In a couple of days, they'll both be called to the principal's office, standing up to the mildly impressed hoots of their classmates. If we both keep our mouths shut, we'll be fine, *The Kid whispers to Emily right before she gets up from her desk, her face stricken with the feloniousness of it all, and The Kid knows then that the jig is up. They'll sit her down and tell her they'd been seen, how serious all of this is, about how much trouble a person could get in if it was found out that they'd done something so horrendous, and she'd be singing like the proverbial bird before they could even finish. So when they call for The Kid over the intercom, he's accepted his fate, such as it is, because it's always easier to accept one's fate when completely inexperienced in* real-world concepts *and* real-world consequences. *He stands in front of the principal with a youthful arrogance and claims sole responsibility for the vandalism with pride, but he's shocked when he finds out how serious all of it really is, shocked when they mention expulsion, completely taken aback when they sit him in front of an Army recruiter right after school and start saying shit like* felony *and* jail time *and* consequences—*and but then, shit like* opportunities *and* duty *and* service to one's country, *and something about an acronym,* LDRSHIP, *which the recruiter brings up time and time again, his bread-and-butter, as he and the principal work hard on getting The Kid to* do his part *and become* Army Strong. *And eventually, he caves. They get The Kid's signature, the recruiter and the principal smiling at each other proudly, what a job well done, and it's only after The Kid puts down his pen that the recruiter bothers to tell him about something called a* troop surge *that's supposed to be happening soon,* per the commander-in-chief—*the recruiter says that with pride, as if he knows the president personally—and that more likely than not, The Kid will probably find himself sucking it in the middle of the desert before the end of next year, Serving His Country and* shell casings are raining down on me, bouncing off my helmet and landing on my back and hitting me in the cheek, a couple of them, sizzling and leaving red welts I—

I'm standing in the living room, a little out of breath, with my hands on my hips. The box is overturned on the floor, a weathered hardwood, chipped in places, whitewashed in others, and there's a rug that looks like it's been here since the 70s, sort of white, with blobby flowers, orange and red and yellow. The walls are the green of an off-brand mint-chocolate-chip ice cream that's been marinating in the back of a dead freezer in an abandoned house, and the couch, brown and dusty, is prim and showy in the way of couches that rarely bear the weight of a tired ass. There's a bundle of fur shivering in the middle of the rug like the A/C is on, which belies the fact that the house has no central air, belies the fact that the trees outside are rustling with a wind that reminds me of *opening the door of the world's biggest oven, and everything there is burned and—*

"Well?" I say, my loud voice spooking the orange blob on the floor, spooking myself a little, for that matter. "What now?"

The kitten quakes and shimmies, readjusting itself on the fugly rug. I'd gotten home eventually, readjusting my grip on the box too many times, setting it down too many times, down the road and across my front yard and up the front stairs and into the house, where I'd tipped the box, shaking it gently, because there was no way I was sticking my hand in there, not after the murderous rage I'd faced in the ditch. One orange ball had rolled out and just laid there, quivering anxiously. The other one had exploded out of the box like a cannonball, spitting like French fry in hot grease, and gone straight under the couch, where it had been growling tiny growls for the past ten minutes.

I nudge the edge of the carpet, furling back the edge a little. It flops over and hides a couple of the ugly flowers from sight. The kitten rocks back, wide eyes flicking and twitching in their sockets.

"You're okay, little guy," I say, raking my voice free of as much gravel as possible and kneeling within petting distance. "Or girl, whatever. You're alright now."

I reach my hand out, uncertain, stiff and cold like granite, laying it on its small back. The kitten is warm in spite of the shivering—almost hot—and soft. I mold my hand to accommodate the curvature, cupping it slightly, and lift my hand up and down like a lever, patting the orange stain centered in the middle of an already ugly carpet a little too hard, wincing at my own roughness, and adjusting, and then softer.

They are kinda cute. Well, this one is, anyway. But what am I supposed to do with them? I can't keep them. I moved out here to finish writing my book, not to become some off-brand Doctor Dolittle.

Well, and that wasn't entirely true either, was it? I've become so adept at lying to myself that sometimes I forget I'm even doing it. Sure, concentrating on my writing had certainly played a part in my decision to move into this tiny house, but so had being bereft of many other options. No, the real reason I'd moved out here was to distance myself from Jessica, from the responsibility of becoming a father, something that had plagued me with worry since my own shitty experiences as a child.

Even more reason to get rid of these kittens. How many shitty experiences have I had with cats? Hell, me and cats, we go waaay back....

But I'd gone back to get them. Which means they're my responsibility, like it or not. And until I find someone to take them, I'm gonna have to Doctor Dolittle the shit out of this.

"What now?" I say. The kitten flinches away from my voice, my granite hands. "Huh? What the fuck am I supposed to now?"

I bet it's starving. Are you feeding it?

I get up and head to the kitchen. There's nothing in the fridge now but some mustard and an empty cheese wrapper, so I grab the only other edible thing in the house, a half-empty bag of cheese popcorn off the counter. Back in the living room, I open the bag, careful not to crinkle too loud, because lord knows this little thing is gonna have an aneurysm if it gets much more anxious. I toss a few kernels on the floor, three or four, and I toss a few in my mouth too, because why not.

"There you go, eat up," I say, flourishing my hand importantly. "And let's see…" I look at the kitten on the rug with a critical eye, then drop to my knees and put my face to the floor, at a safe distance, of course, and I flick a piece of cheese popcorn at the pair of golden eyes shining there beneath, a stolid and suspicious gaze. "You will be Cat," I say, pointing at the slitted eyes. Promptly offended, the disembodied eyes hiss, and I sit up and back on my heels and point at the shivering blob on the rug. "And you, my anxious little friend, shall be named Cat Jr."

I hear the sound of popcorn crunching coming from beneath the couch. Okay, so they *are* hungry. And cheese popcorn, no matter how delicious and nutritious I find it to be, just isn't going to cut it. Which means the responsibility falls to me. Which means I *will* be counting out change and returning empty beer cans. Which means there's more walking in my immediate future, assuming I can't get Frank up and running, or as up and running as the fucking thing's ever been.

I bet it's starving.

Which ultimately means that even after the shit start to the day; even after going to the interview and completely sucking at it and not getting the damn job; even afterward, when Frank had given up the ghost, thusly pitching me headfirst into a damn ditch; even after leaving the kittens and walking home, and folding to Emily's pressure, and then walking back and getting the damn kittens, yes, that's *plural*; even after everything, fucking *everything*, it's looking like a better-than-good chance that I'll be left to think about all of it with a sober brain.

I'm pregnant.

"GREAT," I say, startling the kitten on the rug once more. "Just fucking great, can't I catch a damn *break*?"

CHAPTER SIX

*S*he's an old flame, so old that it feels new, and that's the problem, *they've got a Before. Otherwise, The Kid's not even standing here, too close to her, so close that he can see the smattering of freckles just below her eyes, so close that he can smell her perfume, and beneath that, soap, and beneath that, her, just* her. *The sun dips lower almost perceptibly, gently brushing the tops of the distant tree line, and The Kid thinks about dipping too, thinks about taking a step back, collecting himself, and maybe then he'll have the intestinal fortitude to do what really needs to be done, i.e. leaving, i.e.* Running Away *again, but there's that Before, and he can't ignore it, can he.*

Can he?

You never called me, *she says, smiling slightly. The Kid feels jokingly admonished.* Don't I remember giving you my phone number all those years ago?

Um. Yeah, I think so.

So why didn't you call?

She's kidding, of course she is, but there's an ill-disguised pointedness to the question, a cloaked dagger, and The Kid feels like maybe the question isn't as rhetorical as he's being led to believe.

Um, I-I'm, *he stutters, cursing his tongue for a clumsy fool.* I'm—

⌒

It's all those years ago, circa 2006, right around Xmas, which is some-

61

thing The Kid only remembers because of how cold winter really is when you're in a set of military ACUs, just the uniform, which, in turn, suggests he was on leave, one; and two, that he was still proud of what he looked like wearing the uniform. Maybe it never fully deliquesced into being not proud of the uniform, or like ashamed of it, because there were definitely times The Kid remembers feeling less jaded about his role in the military, the shitshow. When he'd first joined, when they'd given him those first few sets of crisp ACUs, the folds sharp and unblemished by dust and sand and blood and shit and piss and sweat, in that moment, he'd certainly been proud. He'd worn them everywhere, to dinner and to the mall and home, specifically home, because on some level, The Kid wanted people to know, and like acknowledge in some way, and respect his contribution, *whatever that means. It made him feel like someone, for maybe the first time in his entire life; and it'll take a couple deployments, but in a few years, obviously unbeknownst, he'll begin to shove the uniforms farther and farther into the depths of his closet, when he's not wearing them for drills or field exercises or whatever else; and it'll be even more years, too many, before The Kid admits to himself that hiding them behind piles of civilian clothes hadn't stopped him from nightmaring about some of the things he'd done over there.*

But that's then and this is now, and The Kid's just finished boot camp, so he's home, or like, the place he still considers home. He clings to it, this idea of a place, because it makes him feel better about oh the places he'll go; *and because going places, certain places, is made psychologically easier if one has a place to come back to. A home. The Kid's just hanging out, it's him and a friend from high school, and The Kid is eager to show off his shiny new uniform. Coincidentally, John is eager to show off his shiny new girlfriend, and so, after almost no deliberation, they decide to make the forty-five-minute trip from the shitty little town they call home to the nearest shitty little mall, which has been touted far and wide as a very good place to hang out. He calls her up, John does, calls his girlfriend, and she's game, of course she's game; only but, can she bring her sister? And The Kid shrugs, some little girl? Whatever. So John says* yeah sure whatever, *and they go and pick them up, driving too fast on icy roads and jamming out to some Nickelback and Three Doors Down, the same songs over and over again, blaring out of crackling speakers, shitty music via shitty means. And it's cold outside, but it's hot in the truck, too hot, waves of overheated air blasting out of the dusty vents up front, frying The Kid's face like* opening the door of the world's biggest oven, and everything in there is burned and ruined, *and they are very young and very cool, if extremely naïve, and very okay with it all, a feeling only amplified when John pulls into his girlfriend's driveway, his tires sliding dangerously in every direction but forward, and from the looks on their faces, the girlfriend and her sister, they think it's pretty cool, too. So they get in. And go. And they get there in much less time than it should take, defying death and the law at the hands of a very confident driver (overconfident, some might say), and then there's the inevitable undertaking upon one's visit to the Bay City Mall, which movie to see, because what else is there to do inside this giant fossil that doesn't rhyme with shmanging shmout. The choices are something like Apocalypto and Rocky Balboa and Charlotte's Web and Black Christmas, a few others, none of which look very good, all of which we opt against seeing, and so, we decide to just Walk Around, because there's something delightfully flawed about the whole thing, walking aimlessly and going nowhere and doing nothing, really, just looking at things we'll never buy and laughing at stupid jokes and being very young and very cool, if extremely naïve, and very okay with it all.*

The little sister isn't so little after all, The Kid thinks, or like, not as little as he'd been thinking. She's walking next to him, adjacent and a little behind, kind of hovering there at the edge of his blind spot, which bugs him a little, like a fly buzzing around his head. He slows down to match her gait, putting him in this sort of limbo between walking and shuffling, and he looks at her for the first time, like really looks at her, and sees her. She's awkward, seemingly aware of the fact that she's awkward, and nervous about it, he thinks. Her arms are clamped down by her side, like she's holding a cigarette in each armpit, and she's swinging them robotically. *Perhaps to keep me from seeing the nervous circles forming beneath her arms,* he thinks.

Doing okay? *he asks, trying to sound concerned and unconcerned at the same time.*

Yep, *she says, or rather, she squeaks, seeming for a second like she wants to say more, but then says nothing.*

The Kid nods and shrugs at the same time, which feels like just the right amount of unconcerned sincerity, and he quickens his pace, getting a little distance, not because he feels awkward himself, per say, but because he can't decipher exactly why she's anxious in the first place, leaving him, The Kid, to deal with this steadily intensifying feeling that he actually is *being awkward himself, and anxious and nervous, right along with her, and maybe* that's *why she's acting the way she is.*

Walk, walk, walking. They walk. Stopping here and there, actually buying something, believe it or not, John does, a couple CDs, and then they hit the food court, turning in circles, the four of them, looking to each other for advice or input on which of the Chinese buffet or Panda Express or Taco Bell or Subway is the best option. Eventually, choices are made, foods are purchased, and the awkwardness dissipates as they sit there, partaking in the ages-old tradition of breaking bread. She seems to loosen up, the girl does, which makes The Kid feel less anxious himself, and before long they're joking around and laughing and exchanging juvenile ideas, not just her and The Kid, but all of us, John and his shiny new girlfriend, too. It's the perfect opportunity for The Kid to recite a few things he's learned in basic training over the past few months, like how the acronym LDRSHIP *stands for* Loyalty, Duty, Respect, Selfless Service, Honor, Integrity, *and something else he can't remember, or wait,* Personal Courage, *and they all seem pretty impressed, and The Kid feels pretty impressed, too, with himself.*

Then she's like, but what does it mean? *And he says,* well, it means a lot of things, *but then he gets stuck, because going through basic training hadn't really taught him shit about what* Loyalty *really is; low-crawling with his face in the mud, barbed wire clinging to his ACUs, that hadn't helped The Kid understand what* Duty *and* Respect *really are; and shooting expert at the range and ruck-marching until he felt like he was going to fall flat on his face and just die, what had those things really taught him about* Selfless Service *and* Honor *and* Integrity? *What the fuck does The Kid know about* Personal Courage?

Nothing, not a fucking thing, not right now, anyway, because The Kid's still several months away from deploying for the first of two times, and everything he will ever learn about LDRSHIP *lies dormant beneath those distant sands-* as the sun goes down and stars explode overhead like handfuls of tossed glitter and the landscape begins to cool and dogs begin to bark, rangy mutts, skeletally thin and matted hair and shrill barks and- *He responds with something like,* well, it basically means you never leave a fallen comrade, *but the sentiment isn't based on anything The Kid's ever experienced. It's just another piece of information that's been driven into his head over the last few months. And she says,* well, like ever? No, *he says,* not ever, *and he shrugs again, distinctly aware of the fact that he's shrugging too much, and hoping he looks and sounds like he knows what he's talking about, because it definitely doesn't feel like it, not then, only just eighteen and not really thinking about deploying to Samarra or Baghdad, or going to prison, which is eventually where The Kid finds out exactly what that* LDRSHIP *means, faced with the multi-faceted depth of each word, because they somehow become clearer than diamonds in the complete absence it all. But then she's like,* well, what's never, though, like, what about in such and such scenario? *And he says to her,* no, never, *and he feels a little more confident about his answer the more he repeats it, as if each iteration reinforces the idea that every aspect of* LDRSHIP *can be summed up in those seven words, which it might, assuming one actually understands the real meaning behind it.*

But The Kid didn't.

So they talk and talk and talk, the way people do when they've not yet known each other long enough to prefer silence, both of them feeling less awkward as the minutes tick-tick-tick on by. Then, though, not tired of each other, but tired of this shitty little mall, they're done and leaving, John and his shiny new girlfriend walking ahead, The Kid and her walking behind, discussing things that make both of them feel older than they really are and ignoring what sounds like the very beginnings of an argument up ahead. The cold Michigan sky is layered with thick clouds the color of winter, and it begins to snow a little, dusting her hair and eyelashes a diaphanous white, her cheeks reddening as they walk, seeming to become more and more kissable, The Kid thinks. The parking lot is phasing from a tired black to a more-tired gray, so they bustle, the way people do when the outside is too cold for comfort, and they get in the truck, and The Kid gets in the back seat this time, at ease with her in a way that seems almost too sudden, and John feeds one of the new CDs into a slot up front and twists the volume knob a little too far to the right, and we all nod and smile as Kryptonite *by* Three Doors Down *blares out of crackling speakers. And although it's cold outside, it's hot in the truck, too hot, waves of overheated air blasting out of the dusty vents up front, frying The Kid's face as they huddle closer together, The Kid becoming more and more aware of how close her leg is to his, and they're all very young and very cool, if extremely naïve, and very okay with it all, and they head home, going a little too fast on icy roads and jamming a little too hard to the fuzzy music as they defy death and avoid the law at the hands of a supremely overconfident driver.*

— sorry, *he says, surprised to hear himself really meaning it. She smiles then, rose-petal-pink lips over bone-white teeth, and The Kid finds himself thinking about years ago.*

No need to be sorry, *she says, smiling bigger, laughing a little bit, her eyes crinkling at the corners a little bit.* I'm only kidding.

But the apology does something, lends positive charge to the sub-atomic particles floating in the scant space between their two bodies. Maybe it's the smile, the laugh, the crinkles, the past, something; or maybe it's the allure of the old flame drawing him in like a moth, so old that it seems brand-new; but whatever it is, The Kid finds himself falling, not drifting, falling hard, *and suddenly he's kissing her, kissing her* hard, *and it feels like all those years ago, circa 2006, right around Xmas.*

It feels like before.

CHAPTER SEVEN

In the kitchen, I stir a scoop of instant coffee into a cup of sink water, because the more shit changes, the more it stays the same, and I sip it as I walk into the living room, sip it and stand there, sipping and swallowing waves of lukewarm water that tastes like two asses battling. Cat Jr is nowhere to be seen, presumably under the couch with Cat now. The pieces of popcorn I threw down have vanished, and I can hear a crunch-crunch-crunching coming from the gap between the bottom of the couch and the floor. I sigh heavily and chuck back the rest of the coffee, disgusting, and I toss the cup into the sink on my way to the back door. I'm sure to grab the bag of empty tall boys to the right of the door on my way out—I won't be buying a fucking thing without my recyclables—and I exit the house, a quick *fuck you* to Frank in passing, and I begin the one-point-six-mile trek from my house to the corner store, a trip I've made numerous times before, although never for anything remotely related to cat food.

It's always been alcohol, hasn't it? Borrowing money from Emily under the guise of using it for food; and well, I did *use it for food, some of it. But I'm lying if I say a majority of the money hadn't gone toward getting shit-wasted every night.*

Not completely shit-wasted, though, because it was moreso about getting just the right amount of drunk for the smallest bit of money as possible. Stringing out the addiction, not fully committing to it, *functioning*, as it were. You can get drunker than a skunk on less than five bucks, if you do it right: two tall boys of malt liquor, you drink the first one fast and the second one slow. And this is how it's done, and this is also how I justify it, telling myself that it hasn't started to affect my life negatively, I mean, I'm still *functioning* and all that, ain't I? Getting up at the asscrack of damn to drink instant coffee and work on the book a little bit, early enough to work through the nasty hangover beating me over the head; and every morning, without fail, I'd showered and brushed the smell of last night off my teeth and dressed business-casually and headed into town with a sheaf of resumes. There was no reason to quit because I hadn't even really *started*, right?

I laugh bitterly. *You dumbass. How about the one reason that matters most of all? How about you never should've started back, you never should've taken another drop, no matter* how *bad shit got, no matter* how *thirsty you felt. Fuck you, you deserve prison, the death penalty, you deserve to be fucking Dead, Dead with a capital D—*

The corner store is up the road in the opposite direction of the town, and the trip takes me much longer than usual, partly because I don't have Frank, of course, and partly because I've done enough walking today to be sick of it. I'm dragging ass, trudging down a well-used road that grows progressively less suburban with every step I take, i.e. fewer houses, more cornfields and farmhouses. But the ditch is always there, just to my right as I walk with the traffic, bracing myself against the slap on the back I get in the wake of each passing car. I eventually get there and walk into the store, the A/C shoving me a little as I pull the door open. The inside is small and homey, reminding me of the corner stores down south, the sort of place that sells beer and cigarettes and lottery tickets and worms and not much else. I squeak across the faded linoleum, passing the beer cooler without a glance. There's only one aisle in the place, so I go to the end of it, ignoring the wall of wine bottles behind me—*stroking my presumptive sobriety*, as it were—and on the bottom shelf facing the cash register, there are bags of cat food. The price is godawful. Is feeding cats really this expensive? But the cat on the bag looks happy with his lot in life, almost too happy, like whoever designed it had photoshopped a human smile onto him or something, and so I snatch a bag up and carry it to the counter, passing the beer cooler again, this time with just one look, just a little one.

"Got a cat?" says the lady behind the counter, and I berate myself for not getting the jump on the small-talk with a *Sheesh, it got hot out there quick, didn't it*, or maybe an *I hear it's supposed to rain later.*

"Yeah, I found two of them in the ditch," I say, pointing down the road out the window behind her. I put the bag of empty cans on the counter and lean down to snag a bag of cheese popcorn from the rack just below the counter. "Kittens. I guess somebody dumped them. Can I return some cans, too?"

She smiles. The dimple in her chin splits into two, and they bounce off the tips of her curved lips and up into her round, rouged cheeks. Her green eyeliner clashes horribly with blue eyes behind a pair of glasses that look more like a fashion statement than anything else, and she has overly long fingernails, fake ones, and I press my lips together tightly every time they click against each other, against the counter, against the top of the cash register.

"Oh, somebody dumped them? How *horrible!*" she says cheerfully, as if it's not horrible at all, as if I'm not standing there in front of her with gritted teeth and thin lips and averted eyes, just needing my *shit* so I can go. "I have a kitty at home. He's a dick."

I nod a little, dipping my chin toward my chest haltingly, as if there's absolutely nothing wrong with calling one's pet a dick in a public setting. "That's nice," I say, pushing a few bills across the counter and missing them already.

"You said they're kittens?"

"Yeah, little cats. Kittens."

"Right, well, they might not eat this food, you know," she says, gesturing at the bag between us. "Soften it up and they might, but if they're really little... how big?"

I shrug and cup my hands in front of me. "Yea-big? I dunno. Little."

She nods sagely, the lenses of her maybe-fake glasses flashing, glinting. "Honestly, you're gonna be so much better off with some wet food." She points behind me, one of her fake nails coming dangerously close to my left eye. "If they're as little as you say. I'd hate for you to walk all the way back if it turns out they don't like it. Didn't you have a bike?"

I ignore the question and turn, grabbing the bag of dry food and putting it back. I snatch a couple cans of Friskies off the shelf, a dollar each, so less money than I was about to spend, what a plus, and I smack them onto the counter next to the bag of popcorn.

She smiles again, nodding as she rings up the cans. "Yeah, they'll really like this. It's like crack for cats. Just put some on a little plate for them, you'll see."

"Right. Crack." I eye the total on the register and slide a few more dollars across the counter, the rest of what I have. "Can you tell me how much change I'm getting back?"

She click-clacks at the register a couple times. "I think what you've already given me...plus the cans...yep! So your change is four—"

"Okay," I say. "Just one more thing, I'm sorry." And I turn away from the counter suddenly, surprising myself, and I'm pulled to the back of the store like a magnet. I'm telling myself to stop with every step, I don't need it, *this could be the day you quit, let this be day one, the hardest part is right now, just TURN AROUND AND*—

I pull the cooler door open, hating myself for it, and I grab two of the cheapest cans of malt liquor. There's a hunger gnawing in me that has nothing to do with food, and I speed-walk to the counter, trying to look like I'd really just forgot, trying not to show the losing battle raging inside me, and she rings them up and takes the extra dollars I'd left on the counter, the very last of what I've got.

I take the small pinch of change she offers and grab the bag without making eye contact. She knows. I'm in here buying alcohol with what is very clearly the last of what I've got, she's gotta know.

"Thank you for rescuing those poor kitties," she calls after me as I leave, twiddling her fingers up and down in some semblance of a wave. "Let me know how it—"

And I push back out into the heat of midday.

The Kid hasn't been in prison long, maybe a couple weeks. Time moves in a blur, everything is so streamlined, but he thinks it's been a couple weeks. Long enough to get processed, be assigned a caseworker, and get the general lay of the land. The Kid's job in the military had been just that, getting a lay of the land, so while he's definitely not comfortable, things are going as well as can be expected. He keeps his head down and minds his own business, and when any of his fellow inmates asks him for his name, he tells them Zero, which is a nickname he'd picked up on the bus over here, from jail to prison. The man sitting in front of The Kid had been talkative, upbeat, like they were on a fucking field trip or something; and he'd started the three-hour trip by turning around and asking The Kid his name. When he'd responded with his actual name, Jason (which had gone so well for him in the past, hadn't it), the guy had given him a weird look and said, I didn't mean your govment name. And The Kid had given him a weird look right back, and the sun rose on the guy's face, and he'd said something like Oh this is your first biiiiiiid, damn. When the look on The Kid's face remained, he'd laughed importantly and said, You don't ever go by your real name, not in here. He said, When people ask you for your name, you gotta give them your nickname; like, my real name is—and he leans in—is Corey—and he leans back like he's just told me one of our nation's most treasured secrets—but I go by Grams, because, you know—and he starts laughing—I BE SELLIN THEM GRAMS. And The Kid had asked him, What determines your nickname then, and the guy had shrugged and said, Well, lots of times it's where you're from; and The Kid had nodded and said, Well, I'm from Georgia originally; and the guy had said, No, for sure don't tell nobody you're from out-of-state; near about everybody in here is from right here, North Carolina—he pronounces North with a W instead of an R—and people clique up that way, with people that're from the same area as them—and he'd shaken his head then, real serious—nah, you don't wanna be the odd man out once everybody cliques up.

And so, when they ask The Kid what his name is, he tells them Zero, *and when they ask him why, which they mostly never do, he tells them it's because he's from—what had the guy said,* Oh *Fayetteville,* you from the *nine-one-zero,* man, I know a lot of people from around that way; *and he'd said,* Aight then, your name is gonna be Zero, because you from the nine-one-zero, so now, don't be going around telling people no different, not unless you're one of them crazy muhfuckas who likes the smoke.

So The Kid hadn't. He wasn't looking for smoke, and he wasn't trying to start any fires, either. He'd just been keeping his head down. Minding his own business. And when the other inmates asked him who he was, he'd don the cloak he'll be wearing for the next 51 months, and he'd tell them: Zero. *But that was it. And things went how they went.*

They go everywhere in lines, the inmates do, to and from chow, to and from clothes exchange, to and from haircuts, to and from the canteen, where The Kid is able to use what little money he's brought with him to get things like shower shoes and ramen and stamps—which he uses to send letters, but which also acts as the prison's currency, strangely enough— and a little radio with a clear casing, presumably to prevent the inmates from hiding things in them. So while The Kid stays out of and away from everything, he's forced by the natural flow of things to join these lines and go to the places they will take him; and as the days pass, The Kid slowly stops inwardly referring to the men around him as inmates, as them. *Because The Kid broke the law, too. And he's here, too. And slowly, but steadily, what had been* them *turns into* us. *As time blurs right on by, as things go how they fuckin go.*

Per his caseworker, The Kid is required to join the line going to AA every Thursday evening, it's part of the rehabilitation; and so he does, WE DO, *filing out of the cell block and down a narrow hallway to a small, stuffy room, where there's a wooden podium facing several rows of awkward folding chairs. They file in and down the rows, sitting down shoulder-to-shoulder, and things go the way they go in every single AA meeting anywhere. Somebody stands and the rest of everybody sits, and then the somebody talks, and the rest of everybody,* the rest of us, *they just keep sitting, and trying not to fall asleep in the otherwise quiet, stuffy little room, while the person talking tells his own tale, i.e. how he came to be here, what he did to land himself in such a predicament, what role alcohol played in it, how long he's been sober (which always correlates directly with how long the somebody has been in prison), how proud he is of being sober for so long, and et cetera. The Kid never gets up to talk, he just listens, drawing comparisons between the stories this week and the stories last week, and comparing the stories to his own and being shocked to find the same sort of similarities; and but, slowly zoning out on the whole thing, as the routine stays the same and the meetings stay the same, as the stories stay the same and the people telling them stay the same, no one changing, no one evolving in any way. Until one day, a somebody stands up, this guy who has like four weeks left, who has eyes that are too far apart and lips that are too close together, an ugly guy, but he carries it well. His face is lined with the strategically smoothed wrinkles of an older man trying to appear younger than he really is, and his arms are the reddened-brown of an older man trying to appear younger who has made a conscious effort to be tan. His shoulders are trying really hard to be his defining feature, the way he throws them back in an attempt to accentuate a chest he doesn't have, but they refuse to cooperate. Instead, they slump, lazy and bored. Defeated, The Kid thinks, but this guy, he's saying something different for once, he's buzzing off the high being so close to his release date has given him, and he says his name and says he's an alcoholic and everybody tells him hello, and then he says—*

Lemme just say first, I don't come to these meetings. My name might be on that sign-in paper every week, but I don't think I've been in here twice. I reckon I can admit to that. Everybody does it, cause a motherfucker loves him some stamps, don't he? So we pay somebody a couple flags to some down here and sign your name or whatever, just so we can log some good time and get outta this fucking place a little earlier than we might otherwise. It's the same with those fucking jobs they give us, those little seventy-cents-a-day jobs, don't nobody work these damn jobs for any other reason than good time.

The see-oh on duty perks his ears, drops his right hand to his waist, fondling his pepper spray and nightstick pommel eagerly, almost lovingly.

Calm down, see-oh, *the man up front says, chuckling.* I ain't causing no problems. Anyway. So I don't come because I don't believe in AA. There, I said it. And well, lemme specify. I don't believe in prison AA, the way it exists in here. The idea behind AA is abstaining from drink and coming once a week to be around other people who're doing the same, abstaining, but it doesn't fucking mean anything in here, you know? It's easy to abstain when you can't get the shit, when you're not around it all the time, around other people drinking, the ones who don't have a problem with the shit. Am I wrong?

The Kid thinks about answering, but realizes the question is rhetorical just in time.

We're not pushing *boundaries* in these meetings, these success stories aren't *real*. Honestly, there's no point in showing up here, is there, just to what, sign in on the same clipboard and sit in the same chair? And listen to the same opening statements every week, fucking *fellowship of men*, fucking *strength and hope* and whatever else? Somebody stands up here, and we do the group prayer, this is even if you don't pray and haven't ever, even if you don't get down with any sort of god, but it's a god of one's own understanding, see, and so there's your little fucking loophole. It's all politics, every bit of it. Then the Serenity Prayer, just the short one because nobody here wants the long version; then, what is it, How It Works, The Twelve Traditions, Da Promises, and whatever else. And they ask about any newcomers, and there's always a couple-few, so they ask them do they wanna stand up and introduce themselves, and some guys do and some guys don't. They say whatever they say, *hey my name is Billy and I'm an alcoholic*, or for the more pretentious ones, *hey I'm an alcoholic and my name is Billy and I say that I'm an alcoholic first because I'm very serious about my recovery*; and what do we say, or we don't really say it, but what do we think when that happens? *Sit down, dumbass, no one fucking cares*, and you almost hold it against them, fucking smug teacher's pet sorta thing as it is.

But anyway, that's the way I see it, and damn who cares. Sit here and sip the coffee and nibble at some stale cookies the church down the way has donated, and mostly just whisper back and forth, gossiping like a bunch of them seagulls that show up on the yard at every chow time— *Fuck those seagulls, The Kid thinks*—and they're not paying a whit of attention to what's going on up here, the opening statements and prayers and introductions and shit, the literature, these little fucking pamphlets up here. We're here for the good time, right? The earlier you can get outta this place, the better, right? So we come to these meetings and pretend to listen, and in these instances, I guess pretending is almost akin to the real thing. Because who's to say what's in your head, in your heart? But what makes the whole thing hard, this AA shit, the process or whatever, is sitting here watching the performances, you know, these little self-absorbed shows of one-upmanship, i.e. *my addiction is worse than yours, my story is worse than yours, my alcoholism negatively impacted me more than YOURS ever did.* It's like sitting in on a middle-school talent show almost, everybody so eager to get up here and spill their fucking guts, like they're looking for a damn Oscar or something. Just a bunch of little kids, man, that same innocent narcissism or whatever.

The see-oh relaxes. Riot averted. And he slumps back against the wall, his arms crossed. He looks like he wants desperately to pick his nose, The Kid thinks.

Anyway, so I reckon the real question is why am I standing up here today, right now, and I dunno, to be honest. I'm getting out soon, and this is my last meeting, even though it's also the first one I've actually attended in a while. Headed back to my old life, well not the old life, but probably one pretty similar to it. We all go back to the lives we led before coming here, a life we've mostly forgotten, and what do they say, a history forgotten is a history bound to be repeated. Explains the recidivism rate, I reckon. What is it, see-oh, about 60%?

The see-oh doesn't answer. He looks like he's about to fall asleep, The Kid thinks. Perhaps to dream about picking his nose.

Anyway, I don't think any of us wanted to grow up to be an alcoholic or a drug addict, I mean, and I don't remember thinking about it as a kid. But I maybe it's hard to consider so young, because you see it as just something the grownups do, something done after dark, sure, but normal and not that bigga deal at all. It's the same with smoking, the same with drugs, but I said that, didn't I; and it's the same with a lot of things, I'm pretty sure: sex, fucking rock n roll, driving, whatever. You know? We just don't think about it, and I think that's why addictions and shit hit us so hard when we're older, when we get to an age where these things become more than just ideas. They become really, really *real* and before you know it, that's all there is, all there's ever been, and then you just fucking drown.

Me, I reckon I started drinking when I was a teen, somewhere near the beginning of high school, which is when certain elements of peer pressure really begin to carry some weight. Probably no different than almost everyone who has ever had a drink, or started to drink, or watched their respective habits, alcoholic intake or whatever, slowly go from drinking to Drinking. When you're younger, the alcohol or drugs— or both, pick your poisons—I think it doesn't really take anything from you because there's not shit to take. You've got nothing at that age, no matter how much you think you do, because your decisions have yet to result in anything more than a bunch of very temporary-ass shit that only you and those of the same mindset believe is important. So, alcohol, you know—or whatever it is one chooses to do, which at this point is very temporary, like everything else, and very recreational, like everything else, and very socially driven, I think, like everything else—it starts with wine coolers in the woods behind someone's house, youthful interaction by the light of a virgin bonfire, old friends and at least one new kid, usually, and one's crushes and exes existing together, mingling strangely, and discussions of This and That, shit that doesn't really mean shit. And you pop the top on that bottle and the cap bites at your fingers like they do and your elbow is pointed out like a fucking broken chicken wing and then it comes off, the cap, and there's that punchy hiss echoing in your ears as you raise the bottle and take the first sip of it, and it tastes like carbonation's been added to the lukewarm piss of somebody that needs to drink more water or something, I dunno. But that carbonation is sharp and fucking VIOLENT, man, ain't it? On your lips and tongue, burning a path down your throat to your stomach. And it hits like a cold rock. The nostrils flare. Eyes shine like two faraway stars as you stare blankly at the bonfire, which is roaring angrily now, so close, so hot, TOO hot. And this first drink goes down the way all lukewarm beverages do, slow and a little hesitant and nervous like a mouse, but that's just the first one. The second one goes down like water, and so does the third. And the fourth. And perhaps a fifth one depending on how fucked up you feel like feeling. It's not a big deal, alcohol is just a social lubricant, okay, almost necessary, just something to help you talk to what's-her-face's friend, the one who's just roared into town with her newness, almost as if she's appeared out of thin air and stole your stupid little teenage heart and has the nerve to ignore you entirely while you pound lukewarm wine coolers and wait for the sauce to work its magic. But what you're actually doing is wandering down a dark path in a dark wood with a steadily melting candle, just one, and a dumbass smile on your face; and so this is where the vicious cycle begins, ever onward, but backward, too, ever backward, until suddenly you find yourself several years down the road and the drinking has shed its humble beginnings and become something more. DRINKING. And this is where it starts to become less something you *do* and more something that does *you*. Know what I mean?

The Kid knows what he means. And he knows what comes next, i.e. you pack up and pick up and take yourself somewhere else, saaaay, I dunno, the military. And it's a new city, a new life, new friends, new every-thing, a new YOU, but it's just part of that vicious cycle, you see? None of it's really new. It's just a different form of sameness. And so maybe you end up hanging with a couple of guys who want you to call them The Russians, never mind that they're not Russian in the least, and you're in a third-floor barracks room on Fort Bragg in Nawth Cackalacky, all cheap linoleum flooring and harsh lighting and the smell of daily clean-ings carried out by some of the lowlier soldiers, i.e. you. Your mistakes are made that much more visible beneath the toxic lights overhead, sorta like looking at yourself in the mirror of a hotel bathroom. And maybe one of the Russians asks if you're ready, or like, wants to know exactly how ready you are, and although it's new and maybe not quite like those experiences you had in high school, in the beginning, there's still a good time to be had. There's a sorta camaraderie in doing drugs with other people, doing something considered taboo by the majority of taxpaying citizens, but outta sight, outta mind, as they say, and fuck em anyway. So the lines are laid out and The Russians who aren't really Russian, they're lockednloaded, sights drawn on those white lines, and the rolled dollar bill's aim is fucking keen, lemme tell ya; and one of them, he plugs the end of it into a large nostril but changes his mind, pulls it out and sniffs through each nostril individually, sorta testing, and then inserts it into his other nose-hole, there we go, *and there he goes, dipping his head like a wooly mammoth. He places the tip of the rolled bill a hair away from the end of the nearest white line, and before you can watch and see what he's doing and stow away the information for later, he's done, and the line is gone and all that's left is the sound of this guy sucking it in through his nose, sniffing and snorting so hard his fucking eyes are bugging, bottom lip hanging out and glistening, the layer of fat covering his face jiggling, reddening. So then it's your turn and you're drunk because of course you're drunk and you place the tip of the rolled bill just a hair away from the nearest line. Maybe you fuck it up the first time, the powder punching you in the back of the throat and you start coughing without turning your head away and the rest of the line just fucking vamooses off the counter, drifting to the floor like first snow. And maybe the Russians laugh a little, poking fun, or maybe they're just pretending to poke fun, maybe they're actually pissed about it and they're not telling you, although why wouldn't they, why wouldn't they say they're mad if they're mad? And why are the lights so fucking* bright? *And why can't you just stop sniffing for one minute, why can't you just concentrate and stop snorting, why must your eyes leak like a busted water pipe? But then your head comes around and you shuck off the paranoia if you can and more lines are laid out and you're not drunk anymore, none of y'all're drunk anymore, because cocaine does that, you know? Sobers you right up, better than a cold shower and a cup of jizzy-joe; hell, you can drink all NIGHT as long as you've got some nose candy, some of that booger sugar, what have you. But eventually you find yourself out of the coke, because no one ever buys just the right amount of cocaine, you always run out and find yourself wanting more, and your throat tastes like wet aspirin and you keep sucking gobs of coked-out snot back into your throat,* that's the drip, enjoy that drip, Kid. *Your nose is numb, and so is the entirety of your face and your fucking lips, and the very tips of your fingers are tingling like you've got a cattle prod stuck up your ass, and your mind is just fucking* buzzzzzing, *right, and while it's nothing like back in high school, there's still a good time to be had, isn't there?*

But anyway, *the guy says*. The point is that the whole thing is just this big fucking circle. Because you start out looking for a good time, that's all we're ever looking for, you know, and it's this fucked situation where the snake just keeps eating his own tail, and we never stop looking for it, a good time, and even now—isn't that why we're all here? For some good time? And shouldn't we find some comfort in that, being so alike, being with and around people who've been down the same path, who've ruined their own fucking lives in search of a good time? Hell, maybe some of you do. But I don't. Because I know that the real test is yet to come. This isn't *recovery*, none of us have *recovered*. Our sobriety hasn't faced real-world applications. And how do you know if these meetings are working if you've never put it to the test? You're sober, but you haven't had to turn down a drink yet. Sober, but you haven't had to go out to dinner with friends or family and resist getting an adult beverage with your meal. We're all sober, but not one of us has had to walk by the beer cooler at the store, eyes averted, that anxious feeling in your stomach forcing you to clench your jaws, hanging onto your sobriety with dear life as you try to make it out of the store without going back there and wrenching the cooler door open and grabbing just one or two....

Anyway. I think I'm done. Just... remember what I've said here today. Maybe it helps you when you get out, hell, maybe it helps *me*. I'm a few weeks away from my sobriety being tested like a college student, and if I'm being honest, I'm scared I won't pass. It scares me to think that I might be coming back, that I might be part of that oh-so-high recidivism rate. The fear is natural, and I think it's supposed to be what keeps you sober. Scared of fucking up, scared of letting the alcohol take control once more, scared of ending up back here, and et cetera. But a lot of us are going to try to bury that fear beneath waves of drunkenness, about 60% of the people in this room actually, and not a second of the time we spent sitting in here, stroking our own presumptive sobrieties, is gonna be there to save us when it happens.

CHAPTER EIGHT

They're still under the couch when I finally walk back through the door, sweating like a witness on the stand and mumbling at the doorknob for giving me the same shit it always gives me when I try to unlock it. Not that it really needs locking, because one: I don't have shit to steal; and two: if I did have shit to steal, the odds of a burglar traipsing his happy ass halfway to nowhere just to rob me are slim to none, and slim just left the building.

I head straight to the kitchen, and I pop the top on my first can and gulp it down two or three mouthfuls at a time. *Drink the first one fast.* I toss the empty can into the sink and let out a long belch. *And the second one slow.* I fish the second tallboy out of the bag and pop the top—one sip, *sigh*, two sips, *sigh*.

I set the drink down for the time being and start prepping the cat food. I open one of the cans and give it a smell—fucking horrid—and I dump it onto a paper plate. Then I take a fork and mush the wet food until it resembles a small pile of soft shit, and smells like it too, and I go into the living room, affecting an Indian-style seated position as I begin to waft the not-so-sweet smell of wet cat food toward the dark space beneath the couch.

"Cmere," I say uncertainly. "Cmere, kitty-kitties." As if any kitty has ever cmered when asked to. I set the plate down in the middle of the rug. "Want some crack?"

I peer under the couch. Cat is glaring, Cat Jr is shivering still. And either the store lady had lied about this being crack for cats, or these little bastards just aren't crackheads, because neither of them is moving toward the bowl. But I've done my due diligence, haven't I? I'd pulled them from the ditch, went to get them food, and I'd even prepared and plated it for them. The food might not be great, but the service up to this point has been impeccable, if I do say so myself.

"What else do you *want* from me?" I ask, and I slide the plate a little closer to the couch. "Aren't you guys hun—"

A wad of fur bursts from beneath the couch, spitting angrily, yowling tiny yowls at intervals, one needled paw batting the air in my general direction. It's Cat. I'd learned my lesson earlier, so I scoot back and avert my eyes. Maybe it's just a shy eater. I stare out the window, pretending to ignore it. I think about whistling but decide not to. The way things are going, this thing might consider whistling a personal affront. And it's a minute or two, but eventually the kitten caves, too hungry to continue giving a fuck about me, I guess, and I see it attack the plate out of the corner of my eye.

It? I look at the kitten, whose back is turned at the moment, tail stiff and sticking straight out. *It's not an it. It's a him. You named him, you might as well refer to him by the proper pronouns.*

"Not much of a name though, is it, Cat?" I say. His back legs pop up and he spins around, bouncing here and there like a drop of hot grease. I avert my eyes again. "Sorry. I'm minding my business."

He deflates slowly, still growling, and turns his attention back on the plate. He's knocked it completely over and mushed half of it into the carpet, and he's just sorta snuffling at it, like he's not sure what do to exactly. His paws are covered in wet cat food, and he lifts one to his mouth and starts licking it sporadically.

"You have no idea what you're doing, do you?" I say. He jumps and spits, and takes off back beneath the couch, flattening himself into a skid mark to get there.

It's possible that they don't know how to eat yet. I don't have a wealth of knowledge about kittens in particular, but the easiest explanation is usually the right one. Some *dumbass* had neglected to get their cat fixed, so she'd wound up with a litter in her belly. And when getting rid of them all had fallen just short (two kittens short, in fact), the *dumbass* had dumped these last two in a ditch for me, a *dumbass* in my own right, to come across and pick up and take home. So they probably haven't been properly weaned, which means they'll have to be taught how to eat, and guess who's stuck with teaching them?

"My *dumbass*," I say, but not bitterly, as I had been; more like endearingly or something. That buzz is hitting me, spinning my head a little bit and filling my chest with cold fire, and I stand up, groaning at the pain settling deep, deep within my muscles, but they're good-natured groans. Because the memories of why I'm in such pain are beginning to fade, and a bunch of other memories too, they're bleeding away in clots. And isn't this why we do it? To forget, if only for a little while?

I feel the tall boy on the kitchen counter beckoning me like an old lover. And I go to it as such. I grab the bag of cheese popcorn too, and I go back to the living room and sit down at my writing desk. *If they're hungry enough, they'll eat,* I tell myself. *And besides, this book ain't writing itself, is it?* I open my laptop and peer at where I'd left off last, sipping away at my drink and trying my best to ignore the literal and figurative mess to my left.

For now, at least.

Our presumptive sobrieties, *he'd said. Pfff. What had he known anyway? Sure, maybe what he'd said had been true, and maybe some of it had even resonated with The Kid. But the guy would've been better off just keeping his mouth shut, especially with only a few weeks left, because every bit of information you give out in this place can and will be used against you, only not in a court of law, because even a judge can't save you once you've transferred over to The Yard. They sentence you, transfer you, and after that, they leave you to your own devices, had certainly left The Kid to figure it out as he went along, anyway; and he'd very quickly realized that it was best to keep his mouth shut and pay attention and learn from the many mistakes of those around him, i.e. Getting up in front of twenty inmates and telling them that the sobriety they've been working on for the past however long is merely a presumption, and oh by the way, I've only got three weeks left, I'm short-timing it. Because while giving out any sort of personal information in here is highly inadvisable, revealing your release date is one of the bigger no-nos, especially if it's a close one.*

It's a few days later, and The Kid is lying on his bunk, post-lights-out. The cellblock doesn't get dark, so it's hard to call it lights-out and mean it. There are lights everywhere, tons of them, some above, some on the walls, some glinting off the bulletproof glass of the corridor just outside the cellblock, the intermittent flash of a passing flashlight, and et cetera. He'll eventually transfer to another prison, one with individual cells, and then another, two more before his own eventual release back into the real world, but this prison is set up differently than he'd been expecting. Thick concrete walls and an intimidating amount of bulletproof glass surround bays full of rusting bunk beds. There are lockers at the head of every bunk, they look donated from a local school that may or may not have burned down. There's a tiny TV just to the right of the huge door locking them all in, but it's currently off. And it smells of hot breath, of stale farts and dried sweat, so much so that it's all The Kid can do to not pull the neck of his prison-issued jumpsuit up over his nose.

The springs squeak every time The Kid turns over, so he tries not to, tries to lie very still on his back, pretending to be asleep. His bunkmate, a black guy who hasn't said shit to The Kid and vice versa, he's weighing down the bunk just above The Kid, and the springs, too close to The Kid's face, flex with every snore. The Kid hasn't been on The Yard long enough to be snoring away like some of these guys on the bunks around him. Some of them seem downright comfortable in here, the ones that have been here time and time again, and The Kid wonders if he'll ever get to that point, if he'll fall asleep hard enough to snore at any point in the next four years, my god, four years, and he tightens the arms folded across his chest, holding onto himself lest he sink into an ever-growing puddle of terror and despair.

Suddenly, he hears the squeak-squeak-squeak *of someone getting out of their bunk. The Kid keeps his eyes closed and his arms crossed, feigning sleep, because it's not his business, is it? But he can still hear the furtive movements of someone creeping past the end of his bunk, the* squeak-squeak-squeak *of another someone rolling over in their own bed a couple bunks down, and the hushed conversation taking place.*

I need a shank.

For what?

For what, what do you mean, why does anyone need a shank?

Yeah, but aren't you getting out in—

Can you make me one or not?

The Kid is surprised to hear Mr Presumptive Sobrieties requesting a shank from the cellblock's resident shank-maker. It had seemed like he had one foot out the door—what could possibly be worth sacrificing his release date?

I'm not making this unless you're gonna use it.

I'm gonna fuckin use it, just tell me how much.

It's usually two honeybuns or four stamps, but—

But what?

This one's free. My treat. Just make sure you use the fuckin thing, you'd better not puss out.

The Kid listens as the man's pot of bubbling frustrations boils over. They jumped me, man, held me down to my bunk while this other fucker stole all my shit out of my locker, and they're laughing at me and calling me a bitch and shit, and that's all I can see now when I close my eyes, okay, so fuck a release date, they'll give me a new one when I'm finished using the fuckin thing.

They're just trying to steal your release date, man. *But he stops just short of advising against it.* Okay, so where, then? You doing it tonight?

Nah, in the chow hall tomorrow.

The chow hall, huh, right out on front street.

Yeah. Everybody has to see it. I need everybody to see it.

And you get out in how many weeks, you said?

The Kid can hear the guy stand up, preparing to creep his way back to his own bunk before the see-oh on duty makes his rounds, and he says, However many they give me, that's how many.

The shank-maker gives a low whistle. Do whatever you gotta do, but damn. That's crazy.

Very crazy, The Kid thinks, definitely very fucking crazy. With three weeks left, three weeks? What'd happened to testing his sobriety like a college student, albeit with a 60% chance of failure? Was the fear of getting out so great that he was willing to put it off for a while just to make a point? And what does prison do to someone that they even begin to think like that? Didn't this guy wanna go home? Hell, The Kid might take a shank in his person right fucking now if it meant he could trade his four-and-a-half-year sentence for a three-week one....

The see-oh makes his rounds just a little too late to catch anybody out of their bunks, an offense for which an inmate might find himself sitting in the hole before morning comes, and then it's a cat-and-mouse game of sorts—the see-ohs coming by at intervals, a mattress being lifted, the dull crinkling sound of the mint-green vinyl cover folding back, the low thunging sounds of a bed spring detached, and then the flashlights and key rings make another round, and the hushed voice of a dedicated lookout calls them when he sees them. Then the scraping starts, the sound of metal digging against concrete, short and fast strokes, shisk-shisk-shisk-shisk, *dodging the sound of the see-ohs circling, but only just, and all of it follows The Kid into a light and fitful sleep that lacks the depth necessary to leave The Kid feeling rested.*

There's a sweet spot, something I'm aiming for when I drink, a target I almost always overshoot. In this sweet spot, I am warm, and my skin is tingling deliciously. I grow more and more confident, so confident that the words I'm writing flow fast and smooth, and while the things around me grow fuzzy and the edge of my vision blurs like I'm on the edge of tears, my work shines bright, sparkling like a blood diamond. And maybe the confidence is warranted, maybe these are actually some really good words; but it's much more likely that the alcohol has blurred enough of my past that I'm able to concentrate fully on the present. And this. This is the end goal. The sweet spot. I aim to forget.

I stop typing to take a drink, and I gulp all of it but the last swallow, which I swirl around in the can while I tip back in my chair—*whoa, almost busted my ass*—and peruse what I've written with a critical eye. And I sigh a satisfied sigh. Because it might not be good enough tomorrow morning, when I wake up with a hammer in my head and cotton in my mouth, but it's good enough right now, and that's all that matters in this exact moment.

I click save and shut the computer, and I get up, stretching long and hard. The pain from earlier has melted away, save the occasional twinge, and I suppose I have the alcohol to thank for that too. I relax, still holding the can's last swallow, and I look at the carpet. No amount of alcohol is gonna make it any less ugly, but it sure does look comfortable. Besides the untouched mess of cat food that little asshole mashed into the center of one of the hideous flowers, of course.

"Hey little buddies!" I say cheerily, dropping to the floor and peering under the couch. What was once two kitties has melted into a small, misshapen ball, which manifests perked ears at the sound of my voice so close. "You guys aren't hungry? Look—" and I scoop up a little of the food, brimming with a confidence I wish I had all the time, and I stick it into the dark space beneath the couch. "It's okay, have some."

But as soon as I make eye contact with the orange ball, Cat uncurls himself from around his brother and gets into a crouch. While he doesn't attack, or hiss and spit like he did earlier, his eyes are still brimming with distrust; but hunger, too, so I muster up some liquid courage and I set my almost-empty can down carefully, quietly, and I scooch a little closer, jiggling my hand a little, in a manner meant to make it look more appetizing.

"Here," I say softly, but I stop when he flinches away from my voice. Instead, I find myself clicking my tongue against the roof of my mouth just behind my teeth, a sound meant to be encouraging, I guess. I'm moving closer and closer, now about an inch from his tiny pink nose, and he very suddenly decides that I'm too close, food or no, hungry or no, and he darts forward like a viper, teeny fangs flashing dangerously, and bites the ever-loving fuck out of my fingers.

"Well *damn!*" I say, yanking my hand back a little too late, and I swear a couple times, but I'm laughing, too. "Haven't you ever heard about not biting the hand that feeds you, ya little fuckwhistle?"

He growls at me, but not with much gusto. He's come away with a piece of wet food lodged in his front teeth, it seems, and the aggressiveness bleeds away, the heart of a tiger fading away to show him for what he really and truly is—a scared and confused and hungry little kitten.

"But also an asshole," I say, scooping up another wad of cat food from the carpet and sticking my hand under the couch once more. "And I think you know it, too."

He hesitates, but after a couple minutes of silent immobility from me, he attacks the food again. It's clear that he's figuring out this whole eating thing as he goes along, but a mix of biting and licking and hacking it back up and gagging it back down seems to be working. I can see that he still distrusts me, and he's sure to remind me at intervals with an extra-sharp bite and a growl; but the store lady had been right, it's like crack or something, he just can't help himself. And after a minute or two, the other kitten decides what's good for the goose is good for the gander, and he joins his brother in snacking on my fingers.

But the day catches up to me all of a sudden, and the spinning in my head settles into a dead weight, it's so heavy, and my head lolls back in spite of me, pulling me to the floor. Now it's clear, as I lie here, staring at the ceiling, that my head had never been spinning at all. It was the room that was rotating, the house, the world, the fucking *universe*, and it becomes too much, so I close my eyes and concentrate on the sound of my heart thumping in my chest like an underwater DJ.

"See," I say, my arm still under the couch, although the kittens have long since retreated into the farthest corner away from my hand. "That wasn't so bad, now was it?"

And I drift away, uncertain if I'm talking to them or to myself.

CHAPTER NINE

*A*n August heat fills the block, this cafeteria, adding to the sticky layers coating The Kid's forehead and the walls and the floor, steel and concrete everything, adding to the stifling feeling of being packed into a space too small for this many men. The Kid stabs at the meat patty on the tray in front of him. It thunks against the breading—you call this breading, the shit's like sandpaper—and the meat itself is—he picks it up and snaps it in half—it's a mystery Nancy Drew couldn't solve. He drops it back onto the tray and sighs, but not in an exasperated way, not as if the meat patty (along with a congealing mass of baked beans and a small white square of unfrosted cake that, judging from the grumbles buzzing around the chow hall, may or may not be an actual brick) is the very utmost of his problems. In the grand scheme of things, this terrible meal, one of what'll be—and he does the math real quick—like 46,000 of these trays, it's not something worth getting upset about.

EVERYONE SHUT THE FUCK UP AND EAT, LET'S GO, YOU'VE GOT TWO MINUTES!

The Kid buries his face deeper into his tray and stabs at the patty again, and after significantly less than 60 seconds—

OKAY, ONE MINUTE!

Hey man, that wasn't a minute, you ain't even giving us enough time to eat!

The see-oh standing near the door of the chow hall smiles toothily at the brave soul challenging his ability to count. Keep it up, inmate, and you'll be eating yours in the hole.

There's a light smattering of dissenting opinions, but this is the sorta place where opinions don't matter. Write your fucking congressman, write home and tell mama about it, maybe complain to your cellmate, but you've been otherwise stripped of your right to dissent. You're not a person, a human being; you're an inmate, *merely a number, a statistic, and there's nothing you've got to say that anybody wants to hear, not now, not then, probably never again.*

The Kid's sitting at a stainless-steel table with three other men, all of them hunched protectively over their trays, each of them draped in brown shroud, baggy jumpsuits. Everything is calculated to make them feel small. The Kid's been here for some weeks already, but he doesn't know the men seated with him. He hasn't tried, but this isn't the place for getting to know a body anyway. The man—nay, for they are no longer men, *they are* inmates—*the inmate to The Kid's left is white. The one to his right is black. And so is the inmate to his right across from him. Because in here, these are things that matter, one's skin color, one's tattoos, one's haircut, one's confidence—or rather, one's perceived confidence.*

The Kid scoops up a mouthful of cold beans and washes it down with a drink that tastes red. He's not caught up on everybody's names, but if he's learned anything in the past few days, it's that food, unless you have money on your books, is rather hard to come by. He's also learned that buying food from the canteen with the money on your books does not necessarily entitle you to said food. There are perils all around, predators all around, and not just the little-kid kind, and if an inmate wants to purchase food to sate the aching pangs left behind after each meal, he must first invest in a lock for the poorly painted locker positioned at the head of the bunk he shares with another inmate. A lock that can be broken rather easily, given the right sort of initiative, i.e. desperate hunger, or perhaps kleptomania.

The Kid takes another bite. Two more. He almost gags as he's washing down the second bite, but manages not to. It's important not to show weakness, even the smallest bit. Maybe it doesn't matter if he gags on the beans, but then again, maybe it does. There's another kid here, white kid, maybe about his age, and he's sporting a couple black eyes and slapped cheeks, because he epitomizes weakness, just looks *like a victim. Sure, The Kid's thought about standing up for the guy, well, thought about it just a little, but the guy's not willing to stand up for himself, The Kid says to himself, and that's no way to go to battle, with somebody who won't even throw a punch for himself.*

Hey. Hey, homeboy.

The Kid looks up.

You gonna eat that cake right there?

The Kid follows the length of the proffered index finger, his eyes landing on the small hunk of white brick sitting on his tray.

Huh? You gonna eat it?

The Kid thinks about whether or not he's gonna eat it. He's not. And maybe it doesn't matter if he gives his cake to this guy. But maybe it does. Maybe he gives this guy the cake and somebody sees it from a couple tables away and assumes the cake is being taken, not given. Maybe The Kid ends up getting the shit slapped out of him like that white boy, where is he, three or four tables down, and maybe this is all just the beginning, the start of an endless cycle that will perpetuate the idea that The Kid's just some punk who lets his cake get taken. Slippery fucking slope, ain't it, and next it'll be the shit in his locker, anything of value, and then his canteen, should he buy any, and then—

OKAY EVERYBODY, GET UP, LET'S GO-LET'S GO-LET'S GO! STAND UP ONE TABLE AT A TIME STARTING HERE, STAND UP! OKAY, NOW MOVE TO THE TRAY WINDOW IN AN ORDERLY FASHION, A STRAIGHT LINE, WHY DO Y'ALL HAVE SUCH A HARD TIME WITH THIS ALL THE TIME, GET YOUR ASS OVER THERE AND—

And that should be the end of it, everybody getting up in a very orderly fashion, one table at a time, not having as hard a time with it as the sweaty see-oh giving directions would have the inmates believe. But the question still hangs in the air. It doesn't really matter how this guy'd meant it at all, whether he'd intended to sound like he was strong-arming The Kid, because prison is all about perceived slights, not actual ones. And it doesn't even matter how The Kid had taken it, honestly. What matters most is how everyone else *takes it.*

Okay, this table, LET'S GO, MOVE IT.

The Kid moves it. He stands up and grabs his half-empty cup of red water and tips it into his tray, splashing most of it over his uneaten brick of cake. He's not a badass, but he can play the part convincingly, so he looks up as he does it, sure to make steady eye contact with the finger-pointing fuck who apparently thought they were homeboys. The guy looks away first, and The Kid revels in what he considers to be a small victory, but only time will tell if it had been the right choice or the wrong

93

one. Maybe the dude lets it go, maybe he doesn't think as much about it as The Kid does, hell, maybe The Kid's completely overreacting; but then again, maybe not, maybe the guy had absolutely been trying to take The Kid's shit, and maybe The Kid's reaction had been just enough to let him and everyone else know that he's not a bitch like that other kid a few tables down, that he wasn't gonna be taken for a ride by fucking nobody, *not with as much time as he has left in front of him, not now, not fucking* ever. *But either way, what's done is—*

Hey, inmate, you need to fucking MOVE IT!

The see-oh's voice is really close behind The Kid, and he jumps a little, but he fucking moves it. He can feel numerous sets of eyes on him, his fellow felons watching as The Kid slips his tray from the table and turns to join the line of inmates also fucking moving it. The see-oh behind him is radiating with impatience, and a little bit of stupidity, just enough to be dangerous, so he hurries himself; but the second The Kid steps into the line, a chaos explodes in front of him, starting as a dropped tray and cup, and then another couple sets clattering together, and then a furious shout and a panicked yell as Mr Presumptive Sobrieties detaches himself from the line, shoves past a couple inmates, and buries the business end of a shank into the neck of another.

EVERYBODY GET DOWN RIGHT FUCKING NOW!

The Kid gets down right fucking now, drops his tray and lies there the way he was instructed on his way through intake, stomach down and arms straight out in front, and it's cramped down there on the floor with everyone else, state-issued shoes kicking at The Kid from all angles as everyone around him drops their tray and gets down right fucking now themselves; and then it's the sound of a scuffle being subdued and the small tinkling of a red shank hitting the floor and a heavy victimy-sorta breathing and the sssshhhhh of pepper spray being deployed and a cacophony of plasticware hitting the floor and shoes squeaking like kicked mice and the rustle of well-worn jumpsuits and, if you listen closely, the growing buzz of an excited population. The whole thing feels common-place, like car accidents. And the buzzing grows in spite of all the orders to the contrary, floating atop the excited bubbling like a froth, and The

*Kid's having a hard time blinking without crying now, it feels like some-
body's come along and spit a bunch of pepper in his eyes, and his throat
has the scratchy burn of eaten fiberglass. All of the see-ohs are yelling and
dousing the carpet of bodies with pepper spray and rattling their batons
in the air, and then more see-ohs break through the chow hall doors like
a wave of zombies drawn to the scent and sound of inmates being dealt
with. There's some sorta siren honking through the place now, emanating
from somewhere outside, and there's this screeching sorta something,
sounds like a million knives and forks scratching against ceramic, lights
flashing in time. Then somebody comes over the intercom and starts
calmly informing everybody that a code of some sort is currently in effect,
so calm, there's no way the voice is anywhere near this fucking pop-up
warzone. The Kid is more than a little worried about getting stepped on,
see-ohs stampeding past him like a herd of underpaid rhinos, so he flat-
tens himself against the floor even more, pulls his arms in a little, situates
himself into even more of a straight line. The struggle between stabber
and stabbed has been quelled, or rather, the stabber has been quelled.
The stabbed is grabbing at his neck like they do in the movies, trying to
press both hands against the impressive leak that has sprung cheerfully
from his thumping carotid-external-jugular-artery-fucking-whatever. It
might be working better if the see-oh wasn't trying to stop the bleeding
with pepper spray and flecks of white spittle, but it's slowing down. Not
stopping. But slowing.*

*And there's a moment where The Kid sees this inmate, the stabbed,
as just a guy, a human being becoming suddenly aware of how worthless
he is in the face of a universe that doesn't know he exists. The Kid sees
the fear, sees his hitching breaths and wide eyes and slippery hands, he's
seen it before and he understands it,* the metallic applause of empty shell
casings hitting the dirt and the punching of aerated sheet metal and the
dullness of pre-cracked glass shattering and—

I wake up choking on my tongue, it's settled to the back of my throat, a lifeless cutlet. I have vague memories of falling asleep on the living-room floor, but sober me apparently dragged drunk me to my room at some point, and I sit up in bed a little too fast, the remnants of my buzz swirling around in my head like earlier's last swallow. The light from the hallway is off. It's dark. And hot, well, like muggy. The window is open and the ceiling fan is buzzing slowly, pulling in the smells of the ditch outside running perpendicular, the hot greens of growing grass and partially submerged toads and the pale grays of passing clouds and gentle gusts of wind, and the sounds of the all of it, pulled in and blended together at the ceiling like a fruit smoothie. I drink it in. Gulp it. Like a man parched, like a lost traveler. Or like a sloppy drunk shaking off the remnants of some much-deserved nightmares, a total wash of a human being, and not a kid at all but a man, and thusly very responsible for the things he's done, as men are.

I sigh and fall back into the bed. It squeaks. My tongue smacks dryly against the roof of my mouth, dry and sticky, somehow both. I work the moisture back into my mouth. Slowly. And I think: How long has it been since I tried falling asleep sober? Not that it's a completely impossible endeavor, but it doesn't help that the best sleeping agent on the market is nearly cheaper than a pack of saltines, just down at your local what-ever. And while it's certainly true that practice makes perfect, it's also true that there's no comparison between the sort of sleep one gets sober and the sort of sleep one gets when one is shit-wasted. You spend so long conditioning yourself, as an alcoholic, drinking on a regular basis and making it a part of your bedtime routine, that getting away from it, a sort of un-conditioning, sounds and seems easier to those who haven't conditioned themselves to need too much alcohol before falling asleep and staying asleep, sans nightmares.

Drunk Me apparently managed to bring the almost-empty can with him to bed, setting it on the nightstand just before passing out, and I reach for it now, pleasantly surprised to feel at least one mouthful of backwash sloshing around in there. I toss my head and fill my mouth to brimming, a large swallow, a polishing. It's the lukewarm of summer darkness. I close my eyes and fumble the can in the general direction of the nightstand. It falls to the floor. And it's as if those last couple swallows were just enough to make me piss myself—my bladder suddenly feels like it's about to absolutely burst—so I heave myself to the edge of the bed. The ceiling fan isn't spinning fast enough to do me any good, I'd take a hot camel fart right now as long as it meant a breeze across my face, and the outside is steadily coming inside, the sound of stale rainwater trickling, crickets chirping, frogs, the sound of a thousand gnats beating their wings.

I lurch from a general seated position to a general standing position, flinging my body into action and hoping it catches itself, and then I'm tracing my way around the room, smacking my ribs right into the side of the fucking dresser, and that calls for a string of curse words violent enough to make a sailor blush. And there's a moment right before I flick the hallway light on, I'm reaching my hand through a doorway I can't see and into a hallway I can't see, but what I can see, for a second, is the fishwhite outline of a dead hand, impossibly pale flesh, fingernails chipped and chunked away and outlined in the black of old blood and graveyard dirt and—

I flick the light on. It's all gone, disappeared the way something disappears when it's never existed, that is to say, gone without a trace. And the hallway light is the color of cold cornbread, but it rejuvenates me like a splash of water to the face. I've come out of the darkness. Once again. I'm never completely certain that I'll resurface. There's always that chance I won't.

I push my way into the hallway. The walls are the kind of green that makes me feel sick, sick*er*, and there's a white line maybe an inch wide separating the ugly top from the ugly bottom. I trace it with my right hand and push into the bathroom, successfully slamming the doorjamb with my shoulder and—"*Fuck!*"—and I grab the edge of the sink, pulling myself into the cramped bathroom. My extremely uncomfortable bladder is driving the bus, not me, and I wonder for a moment if it would've been okay to just piss myself and clean up in the morning, blame it on the alcohol; but I don't think I'm drunk enough to be pissing myself, and besides, here we are.

Everything in the bathroom is small because it has to be, the whole thing is maybe six by six, and whoever designed it had to find a way to fit the amenities of a full bath into an actual half-bath. Hell, it's basically a fucking shoe closet. The bathtub/shower is outlined in mildewed grout, and it's too small to sit down in without jackknifing yourself—bent knees, and chin on bent knees, water that never gets hot raining down on bald head with chin on bent knees—and the faucet drips perpetually, and the breaks of ear-crushing silence in between each drip hurt more than a dresser punching you in the ribs, more than a doorjamb giving you fucking problems on your way by. And the sink, it's a mere four inches away from the tub, and it's layered with an ashy mixture of dried toothpaste and soap scum, and the door almost kisses it each time it's opened. There are a few fat and naked light bulbs positioned just below the ceiling, where the paint is so cracked and peeling like dry lips in winter, and the light bulbs are *way* too fucking bright, so I leave them off. The toilet is so close to the wall and the tub and the door that it forces you to shit sidesaddle, every bit as uncomfortable as it sounds, and if you swing the door open too hard, which I do all the time, it'll smack the pot, threatening to break it, fucking shattered and leaving me with a little shit hole to piss in, sorta like the bathrooms Over There, cramped and ugly like this, but there's just a fucking hole in the floor and some toilet paper off to the side, the latter only occasionally.

Now I'm thinking about having to pop a squat over the shattered toilet bowl—sometimes the beer mixes with some fast food just right and I'm feeling my way down the hallway with clenched cheeks and a fucking prayer—and I start laughing then as I squeeze between the toilet and the bathtub, stepping onto cold linoleum and planting my hand on the wall, feeling the tannish paint crackling beneath my palm, my fingers, because I'm thinking about the sorta trouble I'd be in—running to the bathroom in the middle of the night with the shits and squatting over these shattered pieces of porcelain, this fucking shit hole, and stabbing myself square in the ass with the craggy remains—but once I become aware of the fact that I'm laughing out loud, LOLing as it were, I realize that it's not really that funny after all. So I cough a couple times and stop.

I see through sleep-slitted eyes that the seat is raised, per usual, and I sigh and relax, letting loose a stream of piss that finds its way into the tiny and inconveniently placed toilet almost of its own accord.

And this is where shit hits the fucking fan.

I'm given a couple slivers of a second to process the following: that my piss isn't hitting toilet water with the sound of boiling tea; that the aforementioned piss isn't hitting the side of the bowl either, or the fucking wall, for that matter; and that—and I realize this just as the shit officially hits—the reason the aforementioned piss isn't hitting toilet water or the side of the bowl or the fucking wall, for that matter, is because what I'm actually pissing on—I open my eyes wider and the light in the hallway shines a little less reluctantly—is a wad of orange fur sporting the flintiest eyes and needliest claws I've ever seen.

This bastard is sitting in the toilet.

One of the ditch kittens, it *has* to be Cat, is sitting in the toilet, in the water.

By himself.

Doing what? Thinking about the universe as it pertains to kittens? Cat philosophy? Shaping up some kitty calculus or something? I don't actually know.

Now I'm swearing and my hand is off the wall, and I've got both hands on my shifter as I try to direct my stream away from the little weirdo. I'm backing away at the same time, I really am pissing on the wall now, and I'm trying simultaneously (and desperately) to pinch off my stream. This piss-whistle, he launches himself out of the water, he's spraying toilet water and flecks of homicidal spittle all of the place, and it's like one of those nature films or something, you see the bear coming up outta the water like the second coming of Jesus, I mean, all we're missing is a voiceover from David Attenborough.

Then everything just sorta screeeeeeches. To. A. Halt.

It *is* Cat, because *of course* it is, and he's just sorta hovering there above the toilet, ears laid back, eyes bugging like marbles, mouth wide open—is this fucking thing laughing at me? I can see every single one of his teeth, every single one of his claws, and his tail is flicked out like a wet exclamation point. So I'm pissing all down my front now, trying desperately to crank my manhood in a direction that doesn't involve giving myself a golden shower. My heels have smacked right against the mildewed grout holding the tub to the floor, and there's only way to go, isn't there, because $F = G*((m$ sub $1*m$ sub $2)/r^2)$—where F is the force of attraction between my ass and the tub, G is the universal gravitational constant, m sub 1 is the mass of the first object (me), m sub 2 is the mass of the second object (the tub), and r is the distance between the centers of each object, i.e. not very far—and then, just as quickly as the shit show paused, everything breaks, shatters, and I fall back into the tub, my head rocking against a protruding soap dish, my tailbone jamming into the bottom of the tub like the tip of a jackhammer.

Cat lands on the floor with a wet smack, and he starts spinning his pissy paws against the linoleum. I can hear toilet water spritzing all over the floor, the walls, he's churning his little legs and spinning in fucking circles and grunting like the happiest pig in the very best shit. Then he finally grabs purchase and skitters out the door, down the hallway, screeching his way back into the living room like a girl seeing her best friend in public for the first time since yesterday.

"Son of a *fuck!*"

I'm folded up in the tub like a broken lawn chair, piss is hitting me in the face and it's warmer and saltier than the tears I'd be crying right now if I wasn't so fucking mad. It sprinkles my chin, pattering down my chest and stomach before coming to a complete stop. The hallway light seems to be shining a little more gleefully than before, and there's a weird, chirpy demon growl coming from the living room.

"I knew it," I mutter, fuming. "I fucking *knew* it." Knew what? That I was gonna end up covered in my own piss in the bathtub at midnight? No, but my past experiences with cats should have been more than enough to deter me from once again putting myself in in the path of one of these demons. Fool me once and et cetera.

I struggle out of the tub, grabbing the edge of the sink to haul myself up, and I'm almost back in some semblance of a standing position when I slip, presumably in piss, and gravity takes me down once more. Then here comes this asshole, Cat, sprinting around the corner, and when he sees me falling, he spins around like a broken UFO and takes off once more, back out into the living room as the sound of something breaking echoes in his wake.

I just lie there. Staring at the peeling paint on the ceiling as I rest on the cold floor like a picked flower. *I knew. And I went back to get the bastard anyway. So whose fault is this?*

Mine. I'd very clearly made a mistake. As I am so wont to do. But this one is a fixable mistake, all I've gotta do is log onto Craigslist and—

FREE KITTENS TO GOOD HOME:

I found two orange kittens in a ditch near my home. I can't keep them, would like to rehome them ASAP, $25 rehoming fee for one or $40 for both, SOONER THE BETTER!

CHAPTER TEN

It's the morning after and I wake up from a thankfully dreamless sleep, my head roaring, the inside of my mouth drier than a bone, a few bucks poorer and still jobless, still fucking *unemployed*, and this is when the self-hate usually begins, or maybe after a little—like fifteen minutes, or thirty- at which point I begin to berate myself for being who I was last night, for giving in and drinking again, doing what I told myself I wouldn't, because every time is the last time until the next time comes around.

It's hard to prepare for the urge to drink, though. It's not like there's a warning, a countdown to when the urge will manifest and rise and peak and, eventually, be sated by that which the urge is demanding. It doesn't ask or request or politely suggest. It demands, forceful and all-consuming, and it drags on me until I hit what is more commonly known as rock bottom, and the alcohol itself acts as a hot-air balloon, inflating and rising and lifting me up off the floor of the hole in which I find myself, self-dug, as it were. And if that sounds like justification for the act of drinking itself, being an alcoholic, rest assured, it is. An alcoholic, this one anyway, spends just as much time justifying his drinking as he does actually drinking.

I get up, however reluctantly, and groan and cough my way to the bathroom. Part of me is hoping that last night was just another one of my fucked-up nightmares, but no such luck—the shower curtain is torn down and in the tub, and there are small puddles of piss on the floor, one here, a few there. But the toilet is empty, I'm sure to check very carefully, so I throw down some wads of toilet paper and take my morning piss. Then I put the shower curtain back up, finish cleaning the floor, and I groan and cough my way down the hallway, through the living room without a single glance around for the kittens, and into the kitchen, where I start a pot of coffee. I usually stir up a cup of instant to span the gap between starting a pot of coffee and completion of said pot, a habit I'd brought home with me from prison. It's a disgusting swill, but it does the job, and I stand in the doorway between the kitchen and the living room, my left hand tucked into the waistline of my pants, my right holding a lukewarm cup that I drink from at intervals.

"Pispispispis," I say, and I wait for some sorta response from beneath the couch, anything, because I kinda want this asshole to come out and acknowledge the fuckery he'd been up to last night, i.e. *pisspisspisspiss*. But he doesn't, there's no response, and how would he go about acknowledging it anyway, so I drop to the floor and peer under the couch.

"Of *course* you're sleeping," I say, muttering, but quietly, because the last thing I need is them waking up. They've combined themselves into one again, and if you didn't know they were kittens, you'd probably think they were a hacked-up hairball. I get to my feet, my head pounding ferociously, and tiptoe back into the kitchen, where the aforementioned pot of coffee has finally finished brewing.

But it's good that they're sleeping, unable to disturb or redirect me, because I am but a creature of habit. Probably because I'd spent the past four-plus years stagnating in prison, where establishing a routine is almost paramount to doing time. Because you'll count yourself crazy if you're not careful, and having a routine forces the days to kind of melt in on themselves, becoming like pennies, i.e. useless in the grand scheme of things, and then you can focus your attentions, need they be somewhere, on how many *months* you have left. And counting months is way easier than counting days, depending on how many of them you have, because you don't have to watch the passing time so exactly. Ask anyone how much time they have left, or how much time they got for their particular transgression against society, and they'll deliver said information in months. It's just another coping mechanism though, like establishing a routine made up of habits; but it's widely considered to be one of the best ways to do time, as if there's a best way to sit and fucking rot.

And having done it for so long, it was too easy to bring those habits home, to immerse oneself in the routine and take comfort in the fact that although everything had changed, not *everything* had changed. There was a sense of purpose behind my daily routine in prison, and bringing the habits home was just my way of clinging to that sense of purpose in a time when it seemed I had none.

Anyway, for perspective, mine had looked like this:

Wake up at four a.m. and stir up a cup of instant in the dark using water from the sinks in the bathroom, not the hot-water dispenser in the block, shit's too hot to drink, it'll burn your lips right off. Drink said cup of coffee and mix another mere moments later, sink water again, and turn on my clear-cased radio, headphones in, while I wait for the lights to come on. And when the lights do come on at four-thirty, I put my radio away and put in my earplugs. I spend the time between four-thirty and breakfast call, which is usually a little after five, reading whatever book(s) I'm currently immersed in and ignoring the zombie-like stirring of those who occupy the block with me. Breakfast call then, and I speed-walk to the chow hall to beat the line, because beating the line in the chow hall means beating the line to the bathrooms, which I use every day at the approximately the same time, like five-thirty or something. I secure the toilet farthest from the door and sip another cup of lukewarm instant as I void my bowels and read whatever book I've designated as my shit-reader, directing requests for *who's got next* to the back of a steadily lengthening line that I'm thankful I missed out on. Then I go to work. There's not a huge thought process that goes into deciding who works where, but if you've been at a certain prison long enough and your face is the sort your case manager can put a name to without asking for your OPUS number, and assuming you're annoyingly persistent, you might land one of the more preferred assignments, which is important because, much like in the real world, some jobs are jobbier than others. Some of the jobbier jobs might have you busting your ass along the shoulder of a busy road, walking in a single-file line with a trash bag in hand, sweating like a pig and picking up trash while a see-oh watches and fondles his shotgun, probably just begging for the chance to use it, to blow a hole in an inmate big enough to see tomorrow through. But I work in the prison library, which is where I find myself every morning before it opens, pecking away at an outdated keyboard attached to an outdated computer, working on a novel I've been writing for a few months. This goes on until sometimes eight, sometimes nine. Then I return to my block and participate in count time, which entails sitting on my bunk, reading and waiting for the see-ohs to perform the basic math necessary to ensure that all inmates, those still on the camp and those who've been shuffled out the gate for job assignments that are quite a bit jobbier than mine, are accounted for. This takes anywhere between fifteen minutes and three hours, depending on who fucking knows what, honestly. Apparently two plus two isn't always four. But then it's back to the library, when count clears, and I spend a few hours doing correspondence courses, studying for various college courses via UNC for no other real reason, no real goal in mind, just doing it to fucking do it. Then it's count time again. Then lunch, which I don't eat because it's time to work out, hitting the weight pile during the hottest part of the day, a strategic move meant to ensure that I have full access to whatever weights I need. This takes a few hours, usually, warming up and working out and cooling down. Then I shower, because I like to get in before the inmates with off-the-camp jobs return, and between three and four is when the showers are completely empty. So I wash myself and direct requests for *who's got next* to the back of yet another steadily lengthening line I'm thankful I missed out on. Then it's count time again, so I take a cat nap and wait for the see-ohs to finish their simple addition. Then it's dinner, which I skip unless it's something I feel like eating—a rare occurrence that only happens when the one inmate who knows how to cook works second shift—otherwise, I head straight to canteen and purchase something to eat for later, which I return to my locker; and then I spend the next couple hours making money, i.e. buying and selling stock in certain items, which depends on supply and demand, and interacting with those inmates who've returned from working outside the gate, trading shit like tobacco and stamps and weed and Other Shit, and collecting on debts. Then it's count time yet again, which I spend inspecting my profit margins. Then I toss my earplugs back in and read until lights out, which is when I set my book down, pull my sheet up over my head, and fall asleep in less time than is humanly possible.

Rinse and repeat. Every day. And the months had just tick-tick-ticked away, stay on the tracks and keep on chugging, keep little-engine-that-coulding, and I ignored the distant pinprick that was my release date for as long as I could, a pinprick that looked too far away every time I checked, until all of a sudden it wasn't, it was right there, like a train bursting out of a dark tunnel and taking me with it, but there's no amount of planning or thinking about it that prepares you for being hit by a train anyway.

Maybe I actually did count myself crazy, I muse, pouring myself a cup of black coffee and leaning against the counter with the kitchen window behind me, open, morning's cool hands caressing the back of my head, chilling my neck. *They say if you're crazy, you don't usually know it, but I don't think that's entirely true. I spent the last several years growing a little bit crazier every day. Now I'm completely batshit, I've gotta be to—* and I gesture disgustedly in the direction of the living room.

Some of the habits had changed, but the base of the routine had remained solid: Wake up at the asscrack of dawn and drink coffee; eat and shit; work on the book, for better or worse; do some odd jobs around the house, get a workout in, then maybe a snooze; eat again, read some books; and then bedtime, time to throw myself to the night goblins, and things went how they went, days and weeks ticked by and I barely noticed, being so used to time passing me by like I'm sitting still.

But, unlike being in prison, I wasn't moving toward anything. There was no release on the horizon, not even a distant one, and the further away I got from my time in prison, the more I realized that I'd brought too much of it with me to make any genuine progress in the right direction. And then I'd only further complicated things by riding that wave of irresponsible decisions right to the shores of *fatherhood*, not only as it pertained to the rekindling of my relationship with Jessica, but too, the kittens—wasn't that ultimately the decision I'd made? To be a father figure to these kittens, for better or for worse?

"For worse," I say, inhaling a whiff of myself, the piss from last night having dried into an overly fragrant cologne. "But not for long."

Reminded of the rehoming ad I'd posted on Craigslist last night, I pad softly into living room, which is where I keep my computer and writing desk; not because I particularly like writing in the living room, but because there's basically nothing else in there to take up space, and nothing makes me more anxious than big, empty spaces. I open the laptop and click my way to Craigslist, which has swiftly become my go-to for job-hunting, and checking the website for new job postings had weaseled its way into my daily routine. The sort of people who posted job offers on Craigslist seemed like the same sort of people who might hire someone like me, an ex-con with a *very particular set of skills*; but while a lot of the jobs were manual labor, something I'm familiar with, I was hard-pressed to find anything I knew how to do. I don't know shit about being a mechanic, I can change a tire and maybe the oil, but that's it; I don't have CDLs, and besides, nobody's hiring a documented drunk driver to drive shit around for them; and, as the failed interview yesterday had indicated, nobody was keen on me preparing or serving their food. I don't know, maybe people think catching a felony is contagious or something.

There aren't any new job postings up yet this morning, the new ones really don't start hitting until noon and later. I check my rehoming ad to make sure it's still there and peruse it critically. There had been an influx of posts advertising exactly what I was advertising, a potential rehoming of a cat or kitten or dog or puppy or lizard, whatever, and all I'd really done is copy and paste someone else's ad and changed a few details, adding things like *there are two* and *they're orange* and *found them in a ditch*. It's not my best work, but neither is any of the shit I've written lately. Should I rewrite it?

And change it to what? I take a sip of coffee and eye the couch. *Assholes for sale? Likes golden showers, may or may not have recently received one?*

Nah. It's gonna have to do for now. And while I've got the peace and quiet, I should probably get some writing done, *best work* as an aside. So I crack my fingers and tuck a pencil behind my right ear—*old habits don't die hard, they live for fucking ever*—my head roaring a little more softly now, the inside of my mouth a little less dry now, but the self-hate still there, ever present, ever lurking, and I dive in, deep down, and I swim in a sea of untruths.

The Kid is having a hard time finding work now that he's been offi-cially removed from the military, but it's not hard to tell why, might be any number of reasons. Maybe it's the separation from the Army, gen-eral under honorable conditions, nothing like that big, fat identifier on your DD214 to really draw in potential employers, i.e. Hey, look at me, I wasn't good enough for an honorable discharge, I'm a fuck-up, don't

invest your time. *Might be that, or maybe it's the fact he has no real work experience. They spent all their time and money preparing The Kid for war, and not much of what he learned translates to the real world.* Leadership skills, untiring work ethic, ability to receive and carry out orders quickly and efficiently, *and not much else. His resume makes him sound like a fucking robot, it's really not a wonder he can't find work. And maybe it's not that, maybe it has nothing to do with his military service. Maybe it's the pending charge of second-degree murder, maybe it's the monthly trips to court and the meetings with his lawyer and the prospect of prison time. All they've gotta do is type The Kid's name into a search engine and*—A Fayetteville man has been charged with murder in connection to a crash in which the victim suffered fatal personal injuries—*click-click*—police charged 22-year-old Jason Gregory with second-degree murder in the death of a 27-year-old Fayetteville resident—*click-click-click*—police cited excessive speed and alcohol as factors in the crash—*click.*

There's plenty more, and The Kid knows this because he's spent hours clicking through the internet himself, lambasting himself for being such a fucking idiot and reading the comments, fuck this guy, he deserves prison, he deserves the death penalty, he deserves to be dead, *and et cetera. And maybe they're right, they probably are, but for now, he needs a job, any job. He's walked around downtown with a sheaf of resumes in his hand for hours some days, dropping them off here and there, his pool of prospects dwindling all the while, spending too much time staring at his phone, waiting for a call,* the *call, and trying his best not to dwell on all the reasons why it remains silent.... Yeah, he'll take fucking* anything *at this point*

But all good things come to those who wait, right? Eventually, he gets a call back, answers the phone so fast that he almost drops it, but the call is for a job The Kid can't really see himself working—a vet assistant. Sure, The Kid had loved reading about animals when he was younger, and he'd spent a small chunk of his childhood hoping he'd grow up to do something with animals, *but what kid didn't? He'd thought about being a writer too, all those years ago, but he'd been told he was wasn't good enough at writing to make any money from it, and besides that, writers are fags anyway, and doesn't The Kid know that? And he'd started keeping secrets then, kept all his dreams to himself, and after a while, all of The Kid's secret dreams had dissipated, drifting away into nothing, and he hadn't given a single thought to doing* something with animals.

Until now. Because he'll take fucking anything *at this point. And so he does.*

They give The Kid a couple sets of scrubs for his first day, and he feels fucking weird in them, feels like he looks weird in them, because it's just strange to be in anything other than a set of ACUs, as far as work is concerned anyway. He looks military from head-to-toe, from his haircut to his tightly muscled arms and legs covered in tattoos to the look in his eye, that thousand-yard stare, the one that says The Kid's been places and seen shit, done some shit he can't forget no matter how many beers he drinks, and oh boy, does *he. So he gets there early and just sits in the parking lot for a bit, feeling nervous, feeling sick, thinking about everything he could do wrong today, thinking of everything he's done wrong recently, and he thinks about leaving, just saying* hey, fuck this, it's not for me and that's okay, no pressure, don't sweat it. *But the longer he sits there, the A/C punching him in the face, the July sun roasting his skin through the windshield, the intermittent sound of car doors closing and horns beeping and faraway chitchat, the easier it is to recognize that he's in no position to be turning down any sort of gainful employment, especially not a job as presumably cushy as* something with animals.

He eventually manages to swallow past the hard, dry lump in his throat, and before he can tell himself no, he's out of the car and walking across the parking lot. The heat is beating down from above, bouncing off the black pavement and back up into his face. A thin layer of perspiration breaks out all over his body. The scrubs are pretty lightweight, compared to the ACUs anyway, but they've asked The Kid to wear a long-sleeve underneath, cover up all those tattoos, you know, and he can feel his armpits starting to prickle with sweat. He goes inside the pet store, where the vet clinic is located, the automatic doors whooshing open with a burst of cold air, whooshing shut behind him, and he smiles polite hellos at various passersby, or an anxious tightening of the lips meant to imply a smile. The clinic is toward the back, where there's a young lady in scrubs of her own looking a little too happy for The Kid's liking, as if she abso-

lutely loves her job and wants everyone to know exactly how much she loves it, beaming at everyone, absolutely tickled pink with herself and her current situation, sitting there behind the desk. The Kid approaches slowly, the urge to turn and leave buzzing through him like a swarm of hornets, but before he can pivot and take off, she sees him.

Hello! *she says, smiling too widely. Her teeth are the off-white of eggshells.* How can I help you?

Here for my first day, *he says, trying to emulate her excitement, or like wondering how, and then not doing it.*

She takes in his scrubs for the first time, her face relaxing a little bit, her attitude cooling a little. Apparently, that teeth-grinding perkiness is reserved for potential customers, and The Kid is just a potential coworker. Oh okay, just head on back, *she says.*

This door right—

She points. Yep, right through there.

So The Kid heads on back right through there, and it's fucking mayhem the second he passes through the door: dogs barking and howling, voices chattering about this vaccine and that fecal sample, and it smells god-awful, dog slobber and wet fur and animal shit and piss, and over top of it all is a spiky scent meant to cover up all these smells, failing miserably. He just stands there as the door swings shut behind him, staring and taking it all in, the stainless-steel tables and the kennels full of various thises and thats, cats and dogs and a rabbit and at least one iguana, and a couple computers and what looks like an x-ray machine or something, everything bright and shining and stark—save the hustle and bustle of vet techs doing whatever vet techs do, which seems to include something with a cat and a needles—that doesn't look fun—and The Kid's just standing there, wondering what to do and who to report to, when one of the hustling bustlers catches sight of him.

Hi, Jason? *she says, walking toward him and extending her hand.* I'm Carrie, I'll be training you on some stuff today!

The Kid takes her hand, it's small and soft and cool, and extends what he hopes is a better smile than the one he came in with. Yep, sounds great!

And before he knows it, he's knee-deep in the shit, running around like a vet tech with its head cut off, trying to absorb information at light speed. He's used to the hustle and bustle, but a different sort, and before too long, he's wishing he could just go back to dodging bullets and jumping out of airplanes and helicopters and doing sixty in a humvee through the tiny, dark streets of a foreign city, but that's in the past now, isn't it, and The Kid needs to try to live in the present as much as possible.

Speaking of the present, now Carrie's asking him if he'd mind helping out with a rather large dog because apparently she, a very big she, doesn't like shots. And The Kid wonders what exactly he's supposed to do, because if the dog doesn't wanna be poked, shouldn't she get final say in the matter? But he follows her into the exam room anyway and grabs the dog the way Carrie shows him, just sorta bear-hugging the beast, wrapping his arms around her tightly and trying to ignore the smell of her breath, the dog, and trying to stop her wildly scrabbling paws from catching purchase. And it seems like he's holding her forever before they finally manage to slide the needle in, apparently slow and easy does the trick, you know, because it's The Kid doing the hard part, so what's the fucking rush, right?

Then they're in the back and The Kid feels like he's earned a break, not because he's done anything exceptionally hard, but because he's covered in dog fur and slobber, smells like a dog himself, and there's a long scratch down his left forearm where one of the scrabbling paws had caught and dragged, and if that's not deserving of a breather, what's it take? A lot more, apparently, because before he knows it, he's in the very back with even more dogs, they're barking and howling up a storm, loud vowels bouncing off the walls, the floor and ceiling, and invading The Kid's ears like Genghis Khan. Carrie gives him a bottle of the spiky-smelling stuff and leaves him to it, and the last thing he wants is to be in there with them, but then he is, cleaning each kennel by hand, one at a time, more shit and piss and slobber, food and water bowls tipped over and mixed therein, and by the end of it, he's covered in even more shit and slobber and dog hair, and now he needs more than a fucking breather, he needs himself a drink or four, that's what he needs.

—fuck this guy, he deserves prison, the death penalty, he deserves to be de—

Hey, do you mind giving me a hand? *Carrie says brightly from behind him, and he jumps a little, shoving his guilt down deep before she sees it welling in his eyes.*

I think I'm done for the day? *he says uncertainly, tacking a question mark on the end and looking hopefully at the clock on the wall.* Supposed to get out at—

Yep! *she says, gesturing him over to her.* Just one more thing and we'll get you outta here.

So he goes over to where she's standing at one of the stainless-steel tables. She's still smiling, even after what feels like a very long day to The Kid, not very cushy at all. There's a smallish cat nestled against her chest, pure white and purring and flexing its paws and blinking slowly. So we've got a couple things we need to do here, *she says.* We're gonna draw some blood from this little gal, do a complete blood count and an electrolyte panel, do a couple shots, and then we'll have to express her anal glands.

Express her who now?

She gestures The Kid a little closer, ignoring his question for now as she lays the cat down on the table. So what you wanna do here is this: Just grab the nape of her neck, like so, and the back legs, like this, see, and you just stretch her out on the table and hold her—yep, that's perfect—and I'll collect the blood.

So he does, and it's not so bad, holding the cat, not compared to earlier with Big Bertha, not compared to earlier with the kennel cleaning. The cat struggles a little when the needle goes into her leg, but The Kid's cut out for it, and he quells the movement with a firmer grip while Carrie fills a couple of tubes with blood and sets them aside.

Now I'll just go ahead and give her these shots while we've got her where we need her, *she says, working quickly and deftly and crooning at the cat softly.* Just a couple pokes, little girl, there we go, you're doing good, *and she is, The Kid thinks, it's going alright, and if this is how he's ending his first day, there's a lot of worse ways it could be going.*

Okay, now, *Carrie says, taking the cat from him and cuddling her again.* Now we're gonna express her anal glands, and I'm gonna let you do this one so you can get some experience. We have quite a few cats that come in needing this procedure, so it'll help out a lot if you can learn how, take some of the strain off the vet techs.

Right. Okay. Let's do it, *he says, feeling less ready to* do it *than his tone indicates.*

So what you wanna do, and I'll hold her this time, is put on one of those gloves right there. Exactly. And now you're gonna wanna slather some of this jelly on your pointer finger, okay, and don't be shy with it either, we wanna slip in, do the deed, and slip out.

Do the deed? *He coughs.*

She smiles gently and turns the cat around. So what you're gonna wanna do is, just take your pointer finger and insert it into—

I uh—I'm not—

Right into the anal opening here, okay, and I'm gonna hold her so she doesn't take off, they really don't like this, you know, and—

Am I qualified to be doing this? *The Kid asks, hoping against all hope that there's been a mistake.*

She smiles again, a little grimly, The Kid thinks. And so you're just gonna feel around in there, okay, and at about the four and six, it's about an inch in, you're gonna feel the anal glands. They feel like little grapes, kinda spongy. And you're gonna wanna just press down gently on them when you find them, you should feel them deflating as the liquid comes out, which should be a yellowish-brownish color—

The Kid tries not to gag.

Oh, and I almost forgot, just wrap a paper towel around that finger too, it'll catch the liquid as it comes out and then we can just dispose of it without making a huge mess.

It sounds innately messy, *he says.*

She laughs, as if she's enjoying his discomfort, as if she has no idea what he's talking about. Yeah, perks of the job, right?

If her laughter is supposed to set The Kid at ease, it's not working. This wasn't what he'd signed up for. Or was it? Had he somehow missed it in the job description?

Is there no other way? *he asks, mentally crossing his fingers.* Is there any other method, maybe a tool I could use….

No, unfortunately, *she says, her smile seeming gentler, her voice a little softer.* If there was any other way, trust me, we'd avoid this method altogether.

She hands him the glove and the tube of lube then, sort of ushering the process along, encouraging, and The Kid puts it on, the glove, and deposits a large glob of the jelly onto the tip of his pointer. He grabs a paper towel and wraps it around the base of his finger, and the cat is ready, stretched out and limp in a firm but careful grip, and everything seems to be going relatively smoothly, given the circumstances. So he approaches the cat's rear, his gloved finger hovering just outside, and the urge to leave grows almost to be overwhelming. Because there's nothing wrong with it, people have different jobs and do different shit at those different jobs, but what had happened to presumably cushy, *what happened to this being just* something with animals?

Alright, *she says, even gentler now, if her voice gets any gentler, The Kid's gonna scream.* Here we go.

And there he goes, he pushes his finger forward, and the cat begins to struggle in place, trying to get away, and The Kid understands it, hell, he'd be trying to get away too. But his finger slips in, and there's no sense in crying about it, is there, he's in the shit now. So he's feeling around, just sorta digging around in there, the cat's making some weird growling noises now, it sounds like an exorcism is in progress—and he feels the first one, and it actually does feel like a spongy little grape.

And I just—

You feel it? Okay, so go ahead and just press on it gently, and you should feel it pop.

The Kid presses on it gently, and it does pop, but so does the weasel, the cat, and by some miracle, she manages to get half her body free, she's writing all over the place, and if Carrie was looking to avoid a mess, well, that's a wrap, isn't it, because there's yellowish brownish liquid spraying in all directions, fur and cat spittle flying through the air, and there's an ungodly sound coming from the cat, it sounds like a nightmare, like wind roaring in his ears, chilling and ripping and tearing at exposed flesh, and *before he can pull his finger out of the cat's ass, the beast takes matters into her own paws, spins around with frightening speed, with frightening flexibility, and latches onto his arm, claws piercing his skin with ease, and now she's trying to climb The Kid like a tree and he's backpedaling away from the cat, and but, taking her with him as he goes, trying to unstick the monster from the front of him with his spare hand, but she's stuck on The Kid like Velcro and staring up into his eyes with murderous rage and—*

Just one second, *Carrie huffs, and she's doing her best, hair flying in her face, flushed cheeks, trying to get the monster back under control, she's getting a serious A for effort. But The Kid doesn't have* one second. *There's no way he's gonna shake himself free of the cat's horrible grasp, no matter the tears and blood shed, so he takes a risk, lets go and lets god,* but a god of one's own understanding, see, and so there's your little fucking loophole, *and he just goes limp, all of him but his legs, and the beast, sensing his surrender, lets go herself and drops,* hitting the dirt roof like dropped cake batter and—

And it's over.

I'm sorry, it's usually not this hard, *Carrie says, leaning down to grab the monster by its neck and stretching it back on the table.* Did you manage to get both?

No, *The Kid says, removing the glove and tossing it in the trash. Whatever the liquid is, it smells like shit and looks like shit in the places it's landed on The Kid's arm; his scrubs his fucking face. There are streaks of blood all down his forearm, the long sleeves hadn't done much to block the cat's wrath.* No, I don't think I did.

Well, let's—

Call it a day? *And he laughs like it's a joke, and then she laughs too, so he laughs again, but this time like it's not a joke, because it fucking isn't.* I'm sorry, *he says, reaching for the paper towels to wipe at least some the mess off himself.* I think I'm done.

And he doesn't say anything else, lets his walking do the talking, heads out front and goes straight to the parking lot, past the receptionist with the weird smile, and he doesn't wait, just changes right there in the parking lot, folding the scrubs nicely, as if they don't have a bunch of shit and blood all over them, and he's back in his civilian clothes—*a pair of jeans and a shirt and some boots—in no time. And he walks back inside, drops the scrubs at the counter with a weird smile of his own, and he whooshes his ass right on out of there, and it never occurs to him to stop and think for a second, maybe give himself time to process, because he's made up his fucking mind, at least as far as* this *is concerned—The Kid'll flip burgers and sling fries before he sticks his finger in another cat's ass.*

I guess I didn't really mean fucking anything after all, he thinks, shielding his eyes from the sun as he walks to his car without a backward glance. Fucking anything but that.

CHAPTER ELEVEN

I'm writing for an hour or so before the kittens begin to stir in their place beneath the couch. I can see them dipping in and out of my peripherals, venturing out into the open, furtive fuckers, and then back. My pace slows to a trickle, stuttering over words like tires on a roadside rumble strip, *the uh—the um—the, the* fucking what, and I'm losing steam like a hot bath. Each word, it's pulling teeth, it's an act of Congress, it's peeling one's fingernails off one at a time with a set of rusted wire cutters.

I stop every now and then, twisting my eyes in their sockets until I can see the kittens without looking at them directly. There's clearly something about eye contact that just sets the bastards off—well, the one anyway—so I avoid it. Their movements are becoming less furtive, perhaps as they realize that the fat sack of flesh sitting in the chair is otherwise occupied. They rub their noses in what's left of the cat food, no longer wet, dried now, and probably not that good, not that it'd been downright delicious to being with, and they chirp at each other, gargling kitty spit in their throats, and they begin to cut tight circles on the carpet, mini-burnouts. At first glance, they look exactly the same: tiny and clumsy with orange fur that makes them look perpetually shocked, but the longer I watch them, it's clear to see that they couldn't be more different. Cat is significantly bigger, and Cat Jr looks like he may have been the runt of the litter, and he's catching hell for it, getting the worst of Cat's impromptu attacks. They both have no idea what they're doing, but Cat does it with more confidence, or like, this unnecessary flair—youthful arrogance—and Cat Jr seems more timid, cautious, and it's clear that he takes cues from his asshole brother.

"Bad influence," I say, and I laugh as my voice sends them scattering back under the couch like marbles.

I look back at my work, reading over it and growing more disgusted with every word. *Sable Valley.* Horror, I think, but who knows. It's fucking horrible, I know that. I've been working on the same book for a couple years now, starting in prison with nothing but a pencil and paper with lines on only one side, business on the front, party on the back, and I'd just kept it going after my release, just one of those habits. I've got no idea where it's going, but it comforts me to keep at it, to have something to hang onto, and perhaps that's why I find myself floundering so much, just as clueless as Cat and Cat Jr, because I'm no longer writing because I want to, but because I have to, for more reasons than one.

And besides, writers are fags anyway, and doesn't The Kid know that?

I backspace away about half the words I've written this morning, slap the computer shut, and sit back in my chair, crossing my arms. It creaks laboriously. Nothing's getting done. I look out the window to my left, lifting the front legs of the chair off the floor and balancing expertly, and I consider flashing back again, but don't. I spend a majority of my time in the past, as if it helps anything, and any time I can resist the urge, I do.

So I'm resisting the urge and leaning back in my chair and chewing on the inside of my lip like a wad of Hubba Bubba, thinking about not thinking, trying not to think, when I see one of the kittens popping a squat on the carpet where the food had been.

"*Hey!*" I shout, and I fling my arms up in the air, hoping to scare Cat Jr out of shitting, but I'm gravity's bitch, and she takes me down again, body-slamming me to the floor as the chair's last two legs kick out like they're greased. "*Fuck!*" The wind's knocked outta me, and I didn't scare the bastard out of shitting, I scared the shit *out* of him, terrified him into shitting all over the carpet, and not even in one place, but all over the fucking place, he's dashing hither and thither, and finally, scared completely shitless, he squirms back under the couch with one last brown squirt for good measure.

I throw my arms over my eyes and just lie there, gritting my teeth. The smell of wet kitten shit drifts over to me slowly, as if to see if I'm alright. I'm pissed, but I'm not pissed at the kitten, what's to be mad about, kittens be shittin'.

And I should've given them a place to do it, it's really not rocket science.

But what? A pile of newspapers? I don't have any more money, nowhere near enough to buy a litter box and litter. Would they shit outside if I took them out there?

And left them out there...

I ignore myself, and I climb to my feet for what seems like the tenth time in two days. There'd been a bunch of cat stuff in the basement, hadn't there? In the box I'd dumped out, there'd been some cat toys and other shit, plus there was a cat tree, so maybe—

I look down at the shit-covered carpet in disgust. That's not gonna be easy to clean up. But I'd better do a damn good job, because if the house's owner stops by and sees this mess, she's gonna—

"Shit!" I whisper, rummaging through the boxes. The aforementioned cat toys, the aforementioned other stuff, but nothing that looks even remotely like a litter box. I sigh and place my hands on my hip, turning around to peruse the dark basement behind me. The one light is on, a naked bulb shining like it's been here longer than the carpet upstairs, but it's not doing much to beat back some of the basement's more stubborn shadows. "I suppose I could use a box, cut it up or..."

I step a little deeper into the basement, scanning the workbench covered in tools, and why, I don't know, what're they gonna do, shit on a hammer, shit in that paint pan over there or something?

I pick the paint pan up. It's caked with dried paint, layers of old decisions, but besides a little dust and a couple dents I pop out, it looks enough like a litter box to satisfy my needs. Perhaps not the best option for someone with an actual *cat*, but Cat and Cat Jr aren't actual *cats*, they're just a couple of tiny fuckwhistles that aren't gonna be here long enough to take more than one or two shits. I'll fill it with some dirt from outside, there's a dry, sandy patch just outside the back door, and it'll have to do until somebody responds to the rehoming ad and takes them off my hands.

Speaking of...

I pull my phone out of my pocket, a few notifications, nothing of interest, but there's an email, and hullo, what's this—*Hi, I'm messaging you about the ad you posted on Craigslist for the kittens? I was wondering when a good time would be to come see them,* and he's also included some spiel about getting the kitten for his girlfriend, as if I care exactly why he wants them, as if I care about anything except when and where.

So I respond—*Today around noon would be fine, let me know if this works for you, oh and I do want to make sure about the rehoming fee I mentioned in the ad, it's one for twenty-five, both for forty,* and so that's that, assuming all is kosher on their end, and the self-hate has faded enough that I feel pretty good about myself, good enough to bust out a little jig. Money's tight, and twenty-five bucks will go a long way toward getting me drunk for the rest of the week, and forty—I slide to the left a little and clap my hand against the underside of the paint pan—hell, that'll go a long way toward getting me *really* drunk for the rest of the week.

It's today around noon, and I'm sitting on the porch, which is really more of a stoop, I guess, when a car passes my driveway doing twenty below the posted limit. I can see heads turning, twisting on craned necks, looking and searching, and I think about waving for a moment, flagging them down, and then don't because what if it isn't them, you know, and then I'm just some weird guy sitting on his front-porch-slash-stoop, waving at them like Forrest Gump waved at Lt. Dan from the deck of his shrimping boat. But the car slows and slows, they drive slower the farther they get from my house, perhaps discussing the likelihood that I'm a murderer, and they get a stone's throw away before eventually pulling into a random driveway, and they turn around.

"That'll be them," I say, and I stand up and go inside the house. Every window in the place is open, but the smell of wet, smeared shit doesn't seem to have faded any, even after a pretty intensive cleaning session involving nothing but an old washrag I found in the basement and some hot water, and no help from the culprit, I might add, Cat Jr, who has interred himself beneath the couch and hasn't poked a whisker out since. After which I went out back and filled the paint pan with an inch of dirt, a few tufts of grass and some rocks in there too, but I picked most of it out and patted myself on the back nonetheless, for being so resourceful or whatever, and I smacked it on the floor against the wall just opposite the couch, where the little shit-biscuits had a clear view of where they're supposed to be doing the deed. Maybe it wouldn't do, but it'd do for *now,* and considering the current developments, it might not even matter. They could both be gone within the next little bit. I'm not much of a salesman, but you'd better believe I'm about to Wolf-of-Wall-Street the fuck outta thi—

"*Whoa,*" I say, stopping in my tracks just inside the door. I hear the car returning, slowing, and it pulls into the driveway, tires crunching over gravel-bedazzled concrete, a small horn tooting cheerily, the slamming of a car door, then another, and shoes scuffing hesitantly, as if unsure. "What the ffffuuuu—"

I don't know how this sorta destruction is possible without a stick of dynamite. Dirt crunches beneath my shoes as I step inside fully and shut the door. I flick the foyer light on and fuck, the paint pan they're supposed to be using is flipped, leaning casually against the wall, and there's piss-soaked dirt everywhere. I can smell it. It assaults me. I try to step around the mess, tiptoe through it, and then I step on something that crunches a little, and then squelches, and sweet Jesus, what a horrendous fucking smell. I pick my foot up, leaving behind a green shit imprint on the floor, grimacing disgustedly at the mess smashed into the bottom of my boot, and there are a couple more little turds lying about, here and there, along with the complete contents of the paint pan, dirt and rocks and grass and all.

"Oh. My. Fuck." It's not just the floor. There's what looks like little greenish-brown spots all over the couch. I crunch/squelch a step closer, and sure enough, sure as shit, there's a perfect paw print right smack-dab in the middle of one of the cushions.

Then here this bastard comes—

Cat bolts into the room with his ears laid back, zipping across the floor and between my legs, and his paws are skittering against the smooth wooden floor. He smacks into the couch, and growls at it, like the piece of furniture has done something to personally affront him, and then he digs his claws into it and launches himself up its side like a gecko in midsummer, perching on the top and turning his side to me and arching his bony little body. His eyes are those of a complete madman. And did he just fucking *spit* at me?

"Um, hello?"

The voice coming in through the front window startles him, and he pops up like something's just bit him on the ass. There's a weird chirping in his throat, it sounds like a hummingbird beating its wings underwater, like the battle cry of a thousand squirrels, and he zooms the length of the couch, throwing himself off the edge like a backyard wrestler, and he belly-flops to the floor and he's off again.

I don't have time for this shit, pun intended, so I go to the couch and reach deep within the recess beneath, lying flat on the floor with my face pressed against the stinking carpet and my arm pushed under the couch to the shoulder. I can feel Cat Jr cringing away from my hand, and I feel the hotness of a small hiss dancing across my fingers, but I hurry up and feel for the loose skin on the back of his neck.

"Cmere buddy," I whisper, pulling him from beneath the couch. His mouth is slack and his eyes are distant, but there's a low whine emitting from deep inside him. I tuck him into my chest and dust myself off with the other hand, beating at my shirt and pants hastily as I walk toward the front door.

I'm thought you were about to Wolf-of-Wall-Street the fuck outta thi—

I tighten my mouth into a straight line and yank the door open, but I'm sure to curve the very ends of my lips up into an empty smile just before I step out onto the porch-slash-stoop, pulling the door shut behind me.

They've pulled their car, a silver one, a Honda maybe, into the driveway, and they're standing there, a man and a woman, both of them mid-twenties and awkward in a way that suggests they're just as uncomfortable meeting me as I am meeting them.

"Hey," I say, trying to make my smile big enough for them to see it.

"How's it going? That him?"

I nod and put the kitten down, depositing him a little closer to them. He stumbles a little, a few shaky and uncertain steps, and then he stops and curls in on himself and just huddles there, and we watch him, the three of us, mutually uncomfortable.

"Found him in a ditch, the ad said?" And he turns around to look at the ditch running perpendicular to the street.

"Yeah, but not that one. Just up the way," and I point up the road.

"Well, I bet he's glad you did."

I shrug and nod and smile a little bigger. It feels aw-shucksy, boyish and uncertain, so I stop immediately. "Yeah, I reckon he is."

He looks at me then, the man does. "Not from around here, then?"

He's Italian or something, the sort of ethnicity he makes sure to remind everyone of on a semi-regular basis, proud of a heritage he's probably never experienced firsthand, flying the flag of a country he's never been to. His hair is black, spiky on purpose, and his face is round and likeable, the sort of guy you'd go get a beer with, the sort of guy you'd hang out with just because, maybe. He's short, or maybe like, very average in height, five-sevenish, and he's the sort of stocky that doesn't have to try to be stocky, the sort of build that doesn't need a gym yet. A few forearm tattoos too, khaki shorts and a pair of New Balances that look too new, and suddenly, I'm comfortable. Not because there had been some sort of threatening aura about him that'd neutralized upon looking at him, but because he's just...*familiar* in a way...

"Yeah, nah," I say, smiling in a more genuine way. "Just moved up here from North Carolina, grew up in Georgia before that."

"Oh, man, what made you move up here," he says, his smile also more genuine now. "Gonna get cold, man, just wait, and you're out here in the middle of all these fields? Sheesh! Gonna freeze."

I shrug again and it feels normal this time, not awkward. "That's what they say."

And it *was* what they said, the proverbial *they*, any time I hinted even remotely that it was cold or chilly or cool outside. It's like people from Michigan have this uncontrollable tick, this urge to remind you that you aren't in Kansas anymore, as if anyone needs to be reminded that the winter months bring with them progressively cooler temperatures, or as if this same anyone has suddenly forgotten they're geographically located in a place known for their nasty winter months.

"Oh, look, he likes me!"

It's the woman. Perhaps moreso a girl, she's built like a simple sentence—independent clause, subject, predicate—but one with an exclamation point instead of a period. The exclamation point is her hair, a braggadociously red ponytail threaded with strands of sun-bleached blonde. Her skin is porcelain white and sprinkled generously with freckles the color of wet cinnamon, and her eyes are the green of pond scum in spring. Her chosen attire shows off flamingo-esque limbs, legs and arms that remind me of dripping icicles, slim and pale like that, as she reaches for the orange ball of fur cowering on the concrete at her feet.

"He likes me!"

And it looks like he does, the kitten, I mean, and sounds like it too, if the low purring coming from their general direction is any indication. She picks him up, and she's cradling him now, rocking him back and forth like a newborn baby, something I hadn't considered doing even once since finding them, and oddly enough, the kitten seems to like that, too.

"So, you're saying you're interested," I say, sounding jokey, feeling hopeful. "There's another if you feel like you need one for backup."

"Oh, that's right, the ad did say you had two. Where's the other?" The guy's looking at the open(?) door behind me expectantly, like the thing is gonna come walking out, right on cue, on hind legs with a fucking suitcase in each hand. "Or didja get rid of it already?"

I'm about to ask the guy if he thinks I'd have brought it up if I'd already rehomed the other asshole, then maybe I'd laugh in a way that poorly implied I was joking, but I suppress the urge to be a dick, and I offer one of my signature tight smiles instead, with a barely-there shake of the head. "Nah, still got him. Y'all were the first to respond to the ad, so I never—"

But fuck whatever it was I *nevered*, because here comes Cat. He's managed to paw open the front door, I guess I didn't pull it all the way closed in my hurry to get outside, and he jets out, zipping through the small crack and down the steps, passing all of us in a blur, manifesting as more of an idea than something tangible, the sort of idea a maniac might have.

"Oh," the girl says, exclaiming, pleading. "Oh look, he's getting away!"

"He sure is," I say, unconcerned. I can't muster a single fuck to give. I'm jobless and broke, so broke I can already feel that rehoming fee burning a hole in my pocket, and this little cabbagehead is taking money out of my pocket by making himself unadoptable. "Look at 'im go."

He doesn't go very far, though. He skids to a stop at the base of one of the trees in the front yard, the one closest to us, and skitters halfway up the trunk like a rabid squirrel. There's a gurgling sound coming from the bottom of his throat and his eyes are bigger and shinier than brand-new nickels. His hind-end is whipping back and forth like a severed lizard's tail, quick and electric, and he's got his fucking head twisted around and back, teeth bared and his nasty little tongue flicking in and out like he's at a Kiss concert.

"Well, there's the other one," I say, turning to them and shoving my hands in my pockets, hoping maybe this guy notices how easy it is to shove one's hands in one's pockets when one is broke as fuck and needs to be paid the agreed-upon sum of twenty-five bucks. Or *maybe*—"Y'all interested in both? You can take 'em both for forty, and I'll throw in the food I bought them, too."

"What's wrong with that one?" She sounds concerned, but she's got *I'm ready to go* written all over her face. "Is he okay? Did you give him some catnip?"

"Some fucking what?" My patience is wearing thinner than a fat lawyer with a gypsy hex on him.

"You know, like…cats, they…" Her voice trails off.

"No, he hasn't had anything but some wet cat food." I point at Cat, who's now cutting circles on the small lawn like a z-turn. "Well, that one, he likes himself some cheese popcorn."

"Popcorn?"

"*Cheese* popcorn," I say pettily, as if it makes a difference. "Before I had the cat food. Anyway, they eat fine. The one you're holding might need a little help, but they eat alright."

"I don't think they're supposed to eat popcorn, though…."

Her voice trails off again, and quite suddenly, I'm very tired of everything, her half-baked sentences, this empty back-and-forth, the niceties and socially acceptable normalities and formal doings expected of one in such situations, and I find myself just wanting it to be over.

"So not the crazy one then, okay," I say abruptly, feeling the sharpness of my own words cut my lips in passing. "That one though, he's all yours."

"Right," the guy says, nodding and looking to the woman for approval. "What do you think?"

Still staring at Cat and his antics—he's back up the tree now—perhaps wondering if it's worth the trouble, she clutches the kitten in her arms a little closer, and nods. "I just feel…."

"Great," I say, pulling my hands from my pockets and clapping a little too loudly. "That's awesome. So, it was just twenty-five for the one then, if you don't mind."

The guy, he digs into his back pocket and pulls out a couple of bills, hands them over, and with tight smiles and a series of overlapping goodbyes that feel more awkward than the hellos had, they're in their car and backing out. I go over to the tree and lean against it, just casual and exuding a *nothing-to-see-here* aura, even as the asshole clinging to the tree reaches out and smacks me in the nose with a needle-tipped paw, even as he chitters and bites at the tree and the top of my head, even as the couple pulls into the street and drives away, their heads turning and twisting on craned necks as they cast a couple more awkward waves and smiles in my direction and speed off.

"Way to go, Cat," I say, pushing away from the tree and starting back toward the house. "Way to fuck up your own adoption." Seemingly unconcerned, he bounces down from the tree and skitters across the lawn, tackling the steps clumsily. I give him a boost to the top step and he takes off again, back into the house, and I follow, chuckling a little in spite of myself. The money in my pocket might have something to do with it, but it *is* kinda funny, in an *oh-my-god-what-the-fuck* kinda way. The amount of energy he has is amazing, admirable even. I wonder for a second at the sorta household he'll ultimately live in, probably a big family, probably lots of kids. He'll be one of like seven pets, they'll have like a bird and a fish and three dogs—one of them's old and one's middle-aged and one's young—and there's sure to be a hamster in there somewhere, whether by design or accident. And this bastard, he'll probably be running the show, he'll be giving everybody what-for if they step outta line, and sleeping in beams of sunshine and breaking shit at will and whatever else.

"And I'll have my money," I say to him, sidestepping another one of his deft attacks. "Everybody wins."

But as the door closes behind me, an oppressive silence descends. The house, a little bit emptier now, leers at me hollowly. And I feel like anything but a winner.

CHAPTER TWELVE

I'm cleaning up Cat's mess, and he's no help, he's dashing from room to room and raising hell. I take a damp rag to the shit-prints on the couch, but it still stinks, and I take a broom to the floor, sweeping around the kitten as he comes screeching back into the room. He starts playing cops-and-robbers with his tail, and I'm careful to avoid his twirling body as I finish sweeping.

I'm pregnant.

I take a seat on the couch and lean the broom handle against my shoulder, clenching my hands in front of me. I've avoided thinking about it for the most part, and this is why, look—the mere thought of those words has my heart jumping around in my chest like this crazed kitten, I think I can feel it touching the back of my throat when I swallow. My eyes are dry and my tonsils feel like hanging coconut. I'm tired, I probably haven't slept more than five a night for months, and what sleep I have gotten has been gotten purely by the grace of grog. I drink a lot of water, but it doesn't solve the sorta dryness one experiences when one's constantly watering one's roots with alcohol. *Aggravating factors* and all that, and speaking of aggravating, here comes this little carpet-shark back into frame, he's boogying through a pile of swept excrement, and I underhand the dustpan in his general direction. It lands on the floor with a smack and he springs into the air, and then he's off again. I hear water splashing. I lean the broom against the wall and rest my face in my palms, they're cold and moist. I rub them all over, dig the heels of my hands into my eyes, stretching my skin in different directions and massaging out what feels like globs and globs of stress. It doesn't do shit for my shoulders, my back and arms and soul, nothing for any of that.

I'm pregnant.

"Pssssss. *Hey.* Fuck off." I grab the broom and poke the handle at the orange bundle of clawed fur attacking the cords running from my computer to the floor, and he fucking grunts or something and glares at me—his entire head is wet, presumably from his quick dip in the toilet—and then he fucks off.

Yeah, hopefully you get to see her as little as possible because lord knows what might happen because are you the sorta guy who can take care of something and be gentle for once and not just gentle with your hands but with your heart too and your mind and your words and basically everything—

No. I'm not.

—you're at wits' end with a fucking KITTEN I mean just look at yourself a KITTEN is giving you fits he's got you up half the night already it's like you've already got a damn baby and you can barely BREATHE man just BREATHE—

I breathe. Gonna think myself into a panic attack. The thirst has become almost overwhelming, as it does when I fall into these ever-present traps. I reach into my pocket and pull out the rehoming fee, a wilted twenty and a crumpled five. They look as dejected as I feel.

I won't spend this on alcohol, I think, wondering simultaneously why I'm lying to myself, as if I don't already know that I'm gonna head back out the front door and start walking down the road, maybe jogging a little bit when I can't see any cars coming or going. Realistically, twenty-five bucks isn't gonna buy much, not once I get some food for myself and more for the remaining kitten and some ~~beers~~, I mean, some litter for his paint pan. Which brings up an even bigger issue: What in the exact fuck am I supposed to do about the remaining kitten?

⌒⟶

So I've cleaned up the rest of Cat's gigantic mess, and he's darted off somewhere, sounds to be in the basement, and I head back outside. I'm not relishing the prospect of another walk to the store, but the money in my pocket provides enough incentive. And I'm walking down the small driveway, I'm thinking about how much alcohol I *won't* be buying, and I hear the sound of another vehicle coming from the direction of Cat Jr's adopters.

Coming back for the other?

I look up just as the approaching vehicle slows, squeaky brakes applied a little too hard, and a purple van with baseball-sized rust holes along the bottom lurches into the driveway like a Ford on four flats. The sky is reflected in the windshield, so I can't see who's behind the wheel, but I'd be a complete fool to think it's anyone other than—

"Jessica," I whisper to myself, saying it like a swear word. How had she found me? Not that I'd been hiding exactly, but I hadn't broadcasted my location either, and for this exact reason: I didn't want to be surprised by the sudden arrival of someone, *anyone*, but specifically this someone, and the fact that she'd found me anyway makes me feel small and cornered.

The driver's side door creaks open and she steps out, or like, sort of rolls herself from behind the wheel. She's breathing a little hard from the effort, her cheeks flushed, her lips pursed around each belabored puff of air, and she closes the door and waddles over to me like a curious penguin. I stick my hands in my pockets to keep me from crossing my arms, perhaps to seem less threatening, and she comes to a stop three or four feet away, cupping her own hands beneath the small planet protruding from her front.

"Hey," she says, trying on a smile. Her hair is up in a ponytail, it's a little longer than I remember—*of course it is, stupid, it grew*—and a different color, I think. She doesn't have any makeup on, and she doesn't need it, not the way she is, bluish-greenish eyes swimming in warm milk and cheeks flushed the color of pink roses and glowing like a dying star.

I mean to respond with a simple hello, but the initial shock hasn't worn off yet, and instead: "How'd you find me?" I blurt.

"Emily."

The Kid knows then that the jig is up, she'd be singing like the proverbial bird before they could even—

"Of course," I say, smiling tightly. I'll have to remember to cuss Emily out later. "What'd she say?"

"Nothing, just that you'd moved out to this place and were trying to finish writing your book."

"That's a fair assessment." Key word being *trying*.

"And that you were looking for a job."

"Mhmm." Key word being *looking*—still.

An awkward silence falls then. I'm not giving her much to work with, but I feel petulant inside, like a kid who, in spite of finding the very best hiding spot, has been found by the seeker with relative ease, before all the other kids. A few cars trundle past, two doing the speed limit, one speeding. I can hear birds and squirrels chattering excitedly overhead, perhaps gossiping juicily about the current happenings just below them.

"You look very—" and I shape the empty space in front of my own stomach with cupped hands.

She laughs and looks down at her stomach. "Yeah, I guess it's been a while since you last saw it."

"Is it close?" I ask, as if the impending birth is the distant approach of an enemy contingent.

She shrugs. "You never can tell with these things. I've felt on the brink for two or three weeks now, but she's taking her time."

And then another silence falls, but not really an awkward one; moreso as if she hasn't finished talking, as if there's something else she wants to say, or maybe ask, but she doesn't, and the silence grows like ditch weeds around the elephant in the room, i.e. Will I be there for it?

Speaking of ditch weeds—

"I found a cat," I say suddenly, scaring one of the nosy birds above off his branch.

"A cat?"

"Well, a kittens, I mean, two kittens," I say, stumbling through my sentence like an illiterate drunk.

"You found kittens? Where?"

"Okay, so, not-so-funny story—" And I tell her about the fuckery of the past few days, leaving out all the embarrassing parts, the parts where I'm still Drinking, sharing the barest minimum, and she's finding it funnier than I ever could. But in the midst of it, I find myself smiling too, with her, and laughing too; not at my own story, but because *she* is, and for a minute, a few moments, it almost feels like Before.

"Wait," she says, stopping me in the middle of the part where Cat decides to destroy his makeshift litter pan, right before the shit hits, as it were. "Is that him?"

I follow her pointed finger to the house's front windows. Sure enough, it's him, bastard son of a bastard son, and as soon as I make eye contact, he jumps up on his tippy-toes, turns sideways aggressively, and falls off the windowsill.

"Yeah," I say, turning back to her, shaking my head. "Yep, that's him."

"So what about the other one, you said there were two?"

"That one is Cat, the other one I called Cat Jr—"

"I see you put a lot of thought into their names."

"Well, see, instead of naming them properly, I posted a rehoming ad. And somebody just left with Cat Jr, I'm sure they'll give him the best name."

"Aw, but that's sad, they didn't want to keep them together?"

"They might've," I say, rolling my eyes, and I tell her about it, ending with, "So they might've thought about keeping them together, but this bastard"—and I jab a thumb over my shoulder at the house behind me—"crashes his own rehoming party and fucks it up."

And before I can stop my stupid hand from reaching into my stupid pocket, I dig out one of the bills- *please be the five, please be the five*—and I hand it to her. "I guess it's best to charge a rehoming fee, supposed to deter assholes who want it for bait or something."

"Bait for what?" She says, reaching for the twenty-dollar bill gingerly, as if it's the *what* in question.

"Fishing? I'm not entirely sure," I say, trying not to stare too hard at the bill she's holding awkwardly, as if she's not sure what to do with it. "But I'm not hard up for cash"—*you fucking liar, what's five fucking dollars gonna buy, you IDIO*—"And I figure you could use it to get, I dunno, diapers or whatever."

"Are you sure?" Perhaps she senses my hesitation.

No.

"Yes, absolutely."

The birds and squirrels overhead have quieted, whether by design or by accident, and I aim my gaze out across the road, past the farm fields laying just beyond, to the set of railroad tracks running parallel to the aforementioned road, and I think, not for the first time, about hopping a train—*the sound of everything around him so quiet, the whispering of Georgia grass brushing against high socks, the distant hush-hush of cars trundling down rain-slick roads, the murmuring of a faraway train approaching, or maybe going away*—you know, waiting until dark and crossing the road and pushing my way through the field's unharvested bounty, walking and walking, much farther than it had looked from the front stoop, until I reached the tracks, conveniently just in time to catch the very end of the train's tail, and I'd reach out, maybe running a little, maybe out of breath a little, and I'd—

"Will you be there?"

I blink a couple times, trying to adjust to the sudden change back to reality. "Be there for what?"

"I meant, I came here to see, to ask you if you'd like to be there. You know. For the birth."

For support, she doesn't say, and the unsaid hangs in the air like smog.

"I'm not sure you'd want me there," I say, or like, mumble, which is easier than telling her I don't *want* to be there, or rather, that I *can't* be, not all of me.

"Well, I have been thinking on it," she says. "And if you want to be there in any capacity, whether in the room or in the lobby, I'd be okay with that."

I'm put on the spot, you know, the one typically found between a rock and a hard place. Half of me wants to be there, knows I should be there, but the other half of me is just as strong, if not stronger—*just look at yourself a KITTEN is giving you fits he's got you up half the night already it's like you've already got a damn baby and you can barely BREATHE man just BREATHE*—and perhaps she can see this internal battle, internal and eternal, because she smiles gently, the same way she always does when she sees me struggling, and says, "You don't have to make the choice now. But I wanted you to know. That I'd be fine with it."

I smile, an empty rictus, and I nod, as if to imply that I'd think on it, leaving not much else to say, and eventually the awkward silence is enough to push her back to the door of the purple rust bucket sitting in the driveway. I think about stopping her, maybe calling out to her—*yes, I'll be there, I wouldn't miss it for the world*—but the words die on my tongue like the first wave of soldiers in a winless battle.

"You know," she says, turning back to me as she opens the door. "Maybe it wouldn't be such a bad idea to keep the kitten."

I snort. "You underestimate how much of a bad idea that would be."

"Well, I just mean that it might help you to feel less alone," she says, and I can hear her voice cracking, but she looks away just in time, stuffs herself into the driver's seat and closes the door behind her, and even with the sky reflected in the van's windows, I can see the first of what'll probably be many tears streaking down her face in rivulets.

I'm pregnant, *she says, but so softly that The Kid isn't sure he hears her right.*

141

What? *He says, and he trains his eyes on her lips this time, watching them press out a P, watching her tongue roll the R, the G coming from the very back of her throat, and then she touches her tongue to the roof of her mouth, just behind her teeth, twice in quick succession, before finishing it off with a sharp T.*

I'm pregnant, *she says, a little louder this time.*

With emotion? *The Kid asks, quoting a movie in lieu of an original thought, and she laughs, but sort of bitterly, and he laughs too, but sort of scared-shitlessly.*

No, *she says, and nothing else, but what else is there to say? It's not fucking rocket science, it ain't hard to figure out—The Kid's an episode of* Maury *away from being somebody's father.*

Are you sure?

She reaches into her pocket—The Kid fantasizes her pulling out a gun and just blowing his goddamn brains out, because what the fuck is he supposed to do now, he's not ready to be somebody's dad, he can't be—and pulls out the proof, the proof is in the pudding, no, the proof is in the pregnancy test, the one she's holding just below his nose—he imagines it smelling of pungent yellow, but these wayward thoughts are nothing but failed attempts at distraction—and the plus sign is a little blurred from being too close, but it's there, there it is, nonetheless.

Oh, *he says, but what he really means is* Oh shit, *because* Oh shit, *what the shit is happening right now, shit just got* real, *the shit has hit the* fan, *and what the shit is he supposed to do* now? *Fresh out of prison as he is, back to Drinking again as he is, and he feels disgusted with himself, that he'd spent the past five years paying for a drunk mistake, only to go right back to the same shit, Drinking again, drunk mistakes again, which makes him feel even more disgusted with himself, referring to his maybe-baby as a drunk mistake.*

In a few months, The Kid will lose a job he considered himself lucky to have found, not because he's been fired, but because he quits, just walks out one day, after months of sticking to it and telling himself that it'd been more than just a drunk mistake and that everything was going to be fine. And when he walks out, he just keeps walking, gathering his things from the place he's been staying, and he'll take a friend of a friend up on her offer of a place to stay while he looks for a job and tries to finish the book he's been writing for the past three years. And when she asks where he went, and she will, many times, he'll turn his phone off and draw in on himself a little more, squeezing his soul down into a painfully tight fetal position, and he'll tell himself that it's for the best, that hopefully he gets to see this maybe-baby as little as possible, because he's not the sorta guy that can take care of something and be gentle for once, and not just gentle with his hands, but with his heart too, and his mind and his words and—

That's all you have to say? *Her tone is pleading with him to say something more, something supportive, something that's going to make all of this better.* Just OH?

The Kid takes a deep breath, trying to collect himself, the shattered pieces of himself, and he clears some of the dust from his throat, and he says—

Oh...my god?

CHAPTER THIRTEEN

In the end, it never matters how many times I tell myself that I'm not going to drink, nor does it matter how convincingly, because I can find a reason to drink every single day, all of us can. So here I am, hunched in my chair with my fingers wrapped around a half-empty tall boy, same as last night, same as the night before, and et cetera. The liquid therein is lukewarm. Bitter. Formerly carbonated, it's flatter than pond water, a disgusting swill. But I cling to it, the buoyancy drunkenness lends, lest I slip gently into dark waters and begin to drown.

I'd barely waited for her taillights to disappear before setting off down the road, and one-point-six miles later, faced once again with whether or not to drink, and *perhaps I shouldn't*, and *I told myself I wouldn't*, but then I'd done it anyway. I'd had just enough for the tall boys and another can of cat food—I breathe a sigh of relief upon seeing a different cashier this time—because the bastard's gotta eat, doesn't he?

And what about you, don't you have to eat?

I tip the can into my mouth again, and I kick the chair back onto two legs in the process. Giving the twenty to Jessica, some sudden desire to Do The Right Thing overpowering me, it'd left me with only a five, sure, but it'd also left me with a choice: hunger or thirst? Because being hungry sucks, but nothing brings on the night goblins like *the thirst*.

Cat is doing some light sprints across the hardwood floor, finishing them off with tumbling flourishes into something or another, knocking it over, more oft than not. Then it's on to the couch, he climbs it like a fat, furry spider, digging his claws in over and over again like a jealous lover attacking a set of unsuspecting tires, and then he clambers to the top, only to fall the very next moment, dropping to the floor with zero grace; and then he does it again. And again. This is followed by the casual punishment of my ankles, and I'm not slick or quick enough to anticipate his attacks and avoid them, so there's me teetering back and forth like the drunk that I am, like Humpty Dumpty pre–Great Fall, and there's him dashing at them, my ankles, with an astonishing amount of expertise. It's built into his fucking DNA, he was prone to murder from the second he dropped, he's not just well-versed, he wrote the fucking *song,* okay? I donate some blood to the cause, hurl some slurred epithets into his destructive wake, and I momentarily consider the spray bottle on the desk in front of me, the one I'd filled after Cat's earlier destructions, fully intending to use it the next time he steps out of line, and with much gusto, I might add. But upon consideration, it *is* outside of arm's reach, and I'm about four mouthfuls of beer from bedtime anyway. I'll be sleeping through the second coming of Jesus, never mind the utter chaos this furball is engaging in, and nothing short of a line of the very finest *booger sugar* is gonna wake me once I wander drunkenly into that Great Beyond. So what do I care? Fuck it up, fuck—

"—it aaalll the way up," I say. Cat ignores me. These words are buried beneath the din of a full trash can falling, the sound of tiny claws scrabbling on linoleum, not in a scared way, in ecstasy, with the sorta excitement that precedes war. And he squirts outta the kitchen and gurgles something demonic in this throat and launches himself into the air in my general direction, but misses, and carries on into the wall, claws scrabbling again, fighting his own kinetic energy and battling his way into more fuckery.

"Fuck. It. Up." I appropriate some culture. I take another drink. "Fuckitup, fuckitup, fuckitup." I shimmy in my seat some. Not quite fucking it up. Messing with it a little. The kitten, though. He's fucking it ALL the way up. He's climbing the walls nearly to the ceiling, he's finding traction on the hardwood by pure determination, he's bursting through the bathroom door and into the bathtub, I hear him, and he's running the inside like an inline skater, the teeth-gritting sound of his shit-kickers squealing up against the shiny porcelain. Then I hear him clambering up the shower curtain, his murdery chirps echoing down the tiny hallway like kicked rats, and there's a small splash, not an ass-over-tea-kettle splash, but a head-dunking evidently, because here he comes, he's tearing back out across the living-room floor like a Mario Kart that's hit a banana peel, spinning in circles and ovals and fucking pentagons and shit, flinging toilet water into the air like a college girl on spring break.

"The toilet *again*? You fuck," I say, and I flap my hand at him, a half-hearted deterrent. He ignores me, and he gets a running start and climbs the couch again, all the way to the top, and then he cuts a triple somersault, his legs flailing hither and thither as he flies through the air, banging to the floor once more.

And then he's off again.

Maybe it wouldn't be such a bad idea to keep the kitten.

"Fuck off," I say. My voice echoes slightly.

It might help you to feel less alone.

I take another drink. "I wish I could be *more* alone."

Keep him.

Hell, I can't keep *myself*, can't take care of my damn *self*, can I? I tip the can again, one last time, and I swallow the end of it, warm dregs of stale beer and backwash, probably moreso the latter than the former, and it goes down with a trained ease. I'm tipping my chair back along with the can, twiddling the empty can in my fingers and holding my tongue out for the very last drops, when suddenly—

There's an orange blur and a *scritch-scritch-scritch* and the sound of trapped meows boiling in hot murder, and Cat explodes out of the woodwork like a serial killer's chainsaw, crashing into the picture with a mortar-like booming, bringing a shower of carefully arranged books in his wake, and they crash and thud to the floor, and my chair tips a little too precariously then, and I rock past the point of no return, and I fling my arms out and my shoulder slams into the floor and I'm rolling and I'm covering my head and I'm *stepping off the back of the helicopter, taking off on a sort of jogging run, and the heat hits The Kid in the face like opening the door of the world's biggest oven opening, and everything in there is burned and ruined, but that's why he's here, why all of them are here, to walk amongst the burning ruins and find something worth salvaging, something that makes them, The Kid and the others filing off the helicopter behind him, feel better about leaving loved ones behind and flying halfway around the world and staying there, in that place, and doing things they'll dream about for the rest of their lives and smelling what Death really smells like: dried sweat and hot sand and oil and grease and gasoline, shit and piss and the blueness of portashitters, which is just the surface, those smells, because beneath it all is the more traditional smell*

149

of Death, blood and hot metal and cold, dirty flesh, among other things. In the end, after it's all done, they'll forget whether War smells like Death or if Death smells like War, which came first, the chicken or the egg, as if it fucking matters, because are they not interchangeable? Then he's running, sprinting as fast as the equipment weighing him down will allow, they all are, and it feels pell-mell and unorganized from his spot in the midst of it, but he knows it isn't, not if seen from above or from the side or from the windows of the houses they're approaching. They run and spread out and infiltrate, stacking up outside of houses and kicking in doors and entering and shouting things like show me your hands *and* don't move *and* come here now, *a crude mix of English and Arabic that sounds like chewing pudding, and there's a few screams, women and children, and there's a wail here and there, a bit of crying, but the operation is organized and efficient in such a way that all the houses are cleared, the military-aged males zip-tied and herded off, the women and children corralled and under a watchful guard, positions designated and taken up, all of this, almost before the thumping of the Chinooks that brought them there fades completely.*

And then they wait.

And so do the military-aged males, and the women and children, all of them. They wait while the questioning of military-aged males begins, is carried out, and is finished. They wait while the Higher-Ups collect SITREPS and radio them back to base, or give the SITREPS to The Kid and The Kid does the radioing back, with only a few mistakes, something he feels good about. They wait while a Blackhawk thumps in and picks up the military-aged males, swallowing them one by one as they shuffle, still zip-tied and with bags over their heads, across the desert fields to the LZ. They wait, everyone, while the sun goes down and stars explode overhead like handfuls of tossed glitter and the landscape begins to cool and dogs begin to bark, rangy mutts, skeletally thin and matted hair and shrill barks is all they are, The Kid thinks, annoying after a while, he thinks, and he's relieved, if a bit naïve, when the barking stops, all of them, one by one, with ear-piercing yelps soaked in red. They wait. The Kid is lying there, prone and uncomfortable on the roof of the tiny house to which he's been designated, and he's sweating and waiting and tired, so tired, and his eyelids are drooping a little, and his right cheek is slick on the butt of his standard-issue, and the red dot in the middle of the sights atop his standard-issue is a little fuzzy around the edges, and wavers a little as the muzzle droops in time with his eyelids, jerking back up at intervals and looking around to make sure he's still alive, that he's not been ambushed in the dark by a towelhead, or even worse, one of the aforementioned Higher-Ups. And he's considering which of the two hypotheticals would actually be worse when one of the Higher-Ups appears out of the dark just behind him, NVGs glowing green and aimed out across the landscape in front of The Kid, scanning and waiting and scanning and waiting.

How's it goin over here, private, *he says, not looking down at The Kid, just scanning and waiting and readjusting his grip on his standard-issue.* Alright, *The Kid says, not looking up at the sergeant, just scanning and waiting himself, and readjusting his grip and his cheek on his own standard-issue, realigning his eye with the red dot and clearing his throat a little and trying to sound very awake and very enthused to be here.* Good, *the sergeant says, glancing down finally and saying,* You just got here, right, in country? *And The Kid says* Yessir, *and the sergeant chuckles a little and shifts his weight, reaching into his pocket and pulling out a tin of Grizzly wintergreen and packing it a few times, holding the tin between thumb and ring finger and smacking the top with his pointer, and then like, half-empty thwacks and the pop of the lid being removed and the sharp smell of fir trees wafting forth as he pinches a wad and packs his lower lip and says,* Don't call me Sir, kid, I work for a living. *And The Kid smiles a little, partially amused and partially nervous about having fucked up, and he says* Sorry sergeant, *and the sergeant nods a little absent-mindedly as he brings his rifle up and sights something out across the desert.* You see that, *he says, gripping his standard-issue and pointing and ejecting a stream of tobacco juice from the side of his mouth. The Kid ignores how dangerously close to him the juice splats, it hits the dirt roof like dropped cake batter, and he looks through his own sights in the direction of the pointed finger, blinking a couple times, salty eyelashes and dry eyes, and fixes the red dot on the windshield of an approaching car. It's a dirty white and small, the car is, and the windshield is layered in desert dust with cracks spiderwebbing across it, so much dust and damage that it's hard to see through the fucking thing, and The Kid can only barely make out that the driver is a woman, the passenger, too, or maybe men dressed up as women, because that's a thing that happens, men dressing up as women to get close enough to The Kid and all of them to throw a grenade, or like, detonate oneself.*

And so, the sergeant says Call it in, kid, CALL IT IN, THEY'RE NOT STOPPING, THEY'RE COMING TOO FAST, *and The Kid fumbles at his shoulder for the mic and he squeezes it and he speaks into it a little too fast, it seems like everything is too fast, the speeding car and the way he's relaying the information to the troops and everything, and he finishes the transmission and sights the car again. It's not slowing, not even when people begin to shout, mouthfuls of chewed pudding, Arabic and English and an ugly mix of the two, shouting and the pointing of standard issues, and The Kid points his standard issue too, so awake now, and so distracted by the pounding of his heart and the fucking fastness of it all that he doesn't even notice the sergeant has dropped to a knee next to him until he feels it jab into his side. He can smell the Grizzly wintergreen even more now, like all of his senses have sharpened to a fine point, and as the car continues to approach, faster now, all The Kid can think about is how the sergeant is kneeling in his own dip spit, and how the stain, dark brown and misshapen and blotchy, how it won't ever come out in the wash, like blood, like how dark blood is when you let it dry, how you never see it when you're out on a mission, never notice the way it flecks your boots and sticks to you almost magnetically, and that's what The Kid is thinking about when the first bullet flies, a warning shot, and that's what he's thinking about when, after the car doesn't stop, a shouted command comes from the ground, somebody down there, a Higher-Up, and the dark and cooled landscape with stars overhead like handfuls of tossed glitter erupts into a din of bucking and spitting weapons, muzzle flashes and the metallic applause of empty shell casings hitting the dirt and the punching of aerated sheet metal and the dullness of pre-cracked glass shattering and, somehow, the sound of sweat trickling down faces like running children and hearts pounding like dropped gavels and teeth grinding and dry lips pressing together like dead leaves crackling beneath shuffling footsteps. The Kid is pulling the trigger on his own standard-issue now, and the butt's punching him in the shoulder chummily, and everything smells hot and dry and metallic. The sergeant's shell casings are raining down on The Kid, bouncing off his helmet and landing on his back and hitting him in the cheek, a couple of them, sizzling and leaving red welts he won't feel until later, and it seems as if it will never end, as the fastness and foreverness of it is expanding at such a rate as to be uncatchable, and all The Kid wants is for it all to be over, fucking done with, and then it just is. The Kid's ears are ringing, and the sudden quietness reminds him of what it feels like to jump out an airplane, the calm after the storm, how silent the world is when one separates himself from everything, the serenity of a fluttering canopy and the distant buzz of a C130 disappearing over the horizon and one's own beating heart and rapid breathing, and a tinny sort of ringing that replaces actual sound, which has all but vanished in the din of war, and things begin to happen slowly, too slowly. The Kid is standing now, probably because the sergeant has him by the collar of his flak vest, and the high-pitched whining in his ears is louder now, bouncing and breaking up into thousands of individual ringings, millions of them, and they begin to sound almost like laughter. The car, what's left of it, is drifting too slowly down the road now, creeping and squeaking and coughing and smoking, too much smoke. The sergeant shakes The Kid a little and he can feel the dry rasp of chapped lips flicking against his ear and the stumbling vibrations of syllables getting lost amidst the millions and millions of chattering laughter, or no, ringin—the ringings. The scent of Grizzly wintergreen is strong in his nostrils, painful almost, and so is the scent of expelled shell casings and smoke and blood and drying sweat and hard-packed dirt, all mixed in a way that forces The Kid to process each one individually.*

The Kid will associate the smell of chewing tobacco with this moment for the rest of his life, but right now, all he can think about is how slow the car is moving and how much smoke is billowing from the ruined engine and how loud the fucking chittering laughter is in his ears as the wind begins to blow too hard. He tries to turn away, can feel the pull of the sergeant trying to help him turn away, but it's too late for that, too late for The Kid to turn away as the flaming car rolls to a shuddering stop at the base of his position, as he sees the way their bodies are pinned against the seats, like they'd been punched too many times to ever get up. He can see their heads, or pieces of them, and flames licking at them hungrily, all of them Dead with a capital D, all of them wilting against each other like melted candles, all of them aerated with ragged and crimson holes, all of them with open eyes and gaping mouths and blood-flecked lips and hair dyed the color of freshly painted fire hydrants and I finally manage to pull myself away, blinking hard and breathing harder, and I just lie there for a minute, gathering myself in the Now and trying to unclench my teeth with much effort and little success.

Cat is nowhere to be found. I look around, wait, there he is. He's perched atop the wreckage—there are novels and textbooks and some dusty self-helps and random magazines fucking everywhere—and he's crouching up there, looking like he's been licking light sockets. He's spitting at me over and over again, maybe super fucking excited about making this bookcase his bitch? I don't know, but my heart is punching me in the larynx and my nostrils are flaring—*dried sweat and hot sand and oil and grease and gasoline and shit and piss and blood and hot metal and cold flesh, cold and dirty and dead fle—*

I shove myself up from the floor, wincing—shoulder's pretty fucked, I'd say, but I ignore it—and I snatch the water bottle from the desk, the one I *should've* used earlier, and I wince some more as I raise it and start spraying at him—*Fuck*, it's on mist—so I switch it to stream and just start *pulling the trigger on his own standard-issue now, and the butt's punching him in the shoulder chummily, and everything smells hot and dry and metallic* and I shove the thoughts away, and I slow down and aim a little more carefully. I manage to peg him in one of his ears with a hard stream of water, but instead of running away, of *course* he decides to launch himself at me. His orange fur is wet and matted—not so much from the water bottle as from the toilet—and his teeth are flashing menacingly, but I sidestep him with the fluid ease of a man much more sober than I, and he flops to the floor, and I'm suddenly so fed up that I can barely stand it, fed up with all of it, all of this, I don't fucking want it, this, it, him—

"*You!*" I say. He's scurrying away from the streams now, and I'm doing my best to empty the bottle. "You fucker!"

You should keep him.

I step to the door in two big strides, and I yank on the doorknob, curse and unlock it, and then I yank on it again, finally managing to pull it open. The heat of the day has dissipated, and the darkness is cooled and moonlit. A couple cars zzzzip by, and I step back into the house, angling myself in such a way that when I resume spraying, the streams push him in the right direction.

"Take that shit outside!"

The open door is like a magnet, he's drawn to that swirling black void like a bat into hell. Maybe the outside calls to him, the horrid little wildling, maybe he hears the call of his ditch. But whatever it is, he's absolutely moving. He growls at me as he passes, and seems to consider giving me a swift bite, but the darkness calls to him like an old friend, and he goes to it as such.

It might help you feel less alone.

I slam the door a little too hard. I snap the locks into place and put my back to the door, and I drop my face into my hands and slide slowly to the floor, almost in spite of myself. The flashback clings to me like a wet sweater. My ankles are stinging like I've been zapped by a bunch of baby jellyfish. I rub my face hard, as if it's a knotted muscle, as if I can massage the problem away, and look up: The chair is lying on the floor, somehow still in one piece, and there are small puddles of water everywhere, missed shots, *the metallic applause of empty shell casings hitting*—no, just water—and books lying hither and thither. All in all, perhaps not the biggest mess the little asshole has ever made, but the most impactful one, to say the least.

Might not be such a bad idea to—

I push myself to my feet, more wincing, more groaning, and I grab the mostly empty can from the floor. It's a miracle, maybe more like dumb luck, but the remaining swallows managed to stay inside the can as I fell, even as it hit the floor and rolled, so I tip my head back now and finish the job.

Keep the—

"Oh, fuck off," I say to no one, and I belch for good measure. I pick up the chair and smack it on the floor in front of the computer, which I open, and I sit down, and I go to the pets section of Craigslist and I begin to type, however drunkenly, the first words of yet another rehoming ad.

CHAPTER FOURTEEN

★ Someone please come adopt this Asshole (Bay city)

image 1 of 4

I found this kitten in the ditch and named him Ditch Kitty. He is not sweet or nice or even the least bit thankful that I saved him from certain death. He's an asshole all the time. Let me tell you about this kitten—

One, never look him in the eyes. The second you do, he loses his fucking mind and for the next three hours, he runs around doing general piece-of-shit things like attacking your feet and chewing on lamp cords and sharpening his claws on all the nice furniture.

Two, he can't just eat like a normal cat. He knocks his bowl over and scatters the food to fuck and back while he licks the bottom of the bowl.

Okay, three, he loves playing in the litter box and tracking his shit all over the house like he's redecorating, and no, I don't love what he's done with the place.

Four, he begs at your feet like an entitled little bastard if you so much as take a drink of water. That's my fault though, because I gave him a piece of cheese popcorn one day and now he's like a crack addict begging for a fix every time I step into the kitchen.

Five, he will not cuddle. Every time you touch him, he attacks you and tries to chew your fingers off, so maybe you could put him near your front door and use him as a guard dog or something, I dunno.

Six, he does no grooming whatsoever and he smells like an old motel room full of sweating fat people, it's disgusting.

Look, I could go on and on about this little asshole, but you get the point. It's like living with Medusa. I peek around corners with mirrors and tiptoe around the house when he's sleeping, which oh by the way, is only during the day. I should have left him in his ditch, but I didn't, and now I'm just begging someone to come and get this kitten before he murders me in my sleep because I don't have any cheese popcorn to give him.

See above for a picture of the asshole in question. He's cute I guess, I'm not really into cats so I dunno. He'll be awake in about an hour, though, and lord help me then.

$25 rehoming fee and you can take all of the kitty food I bought him, too.

CHAPTER FIFTEEN

It's cooler today, made for a decent ride into town, not sweating too much. The air tastes like the beginning of fall. A little crisp. But sitting here business-casually, in an otherwise empty restaurant dining room, waiting for yet another job interview, the sun blasting me in the face does little to suggest that summer is on its way out. I fold my hands on the table in front of me. They tremble a little. I lock them together more tightly. A few more minutes and they'll probably squelch, palms moist and cold like a recent death. My armpits are prickling and I know I'm gonna start leaking like an old tire if they don't come and ask me some fucking questions soon.

I'd passed out the night before facedown on my mattress, with my arms straight down by my side, which I only know because that's the way I'd woken up, like a damp two-by-four, my face sticking to the sheets via an impressive amount of drool for such a dry mouth. After stumbling to the bathroom, and halfway through a thankfully uninterrupted piss, last night's furred fiasco had hit me like a ton of bricks: that asshole kitten, the mayhem, the aftermath, and et cetera; and pieces of the ad I'd written began to sneak through the thick hangover fog pervading my thought process.

SOMEONE PLEASE COME ADOPT THIS ASSHOLE—I found this kitten in the ditch—never look him in the eyes—he begs at your feet like an entitled little bastard—and he smells like an old motel room full of sweating fat people, it's—

I sigh laboriously and just stop myself from punctuating it with a whispered *fuck*, and I tip my head against the sun bursting through the windows as if in search of a vampire, the bill of my hat shading hard eyes and stress-creased face and lips that smile only when they're forced to.

And then I'd hurried to my desk, not bothering to pull out the chair, and I'd popped the lid and logged into my email—*a hundred messages, seventy-eight unread emails, why the f*—and started clicking.

Click. *I would like to adopt the ditch kitty, how soon can we come see him?* Click. *I will pay double the rehoming fee, I love him so much!* Click. *THE CAT'S NOT AN ASSHOLE YOU'RE AN ASSHOLE AND MAYBE HE ACTS THE WAY HE ACTS BECAUSE YOU CUSS AT HIM AND—*

Click. *I know this is a long shot, but do you still have the asshole kitten?* Click. *Has someone come to get that poor kitty? No offense, but I don't think you should be the one—*Click. *Where did you find the kitten and where are you located?* Click. *I hope you burn in hell for talking like that about a little—*Click. *Hi, just wanted to say that your ad was hilarious and I think you should keep him.*

Click.

Something rises inside me, gets stuck in my throat. I feel stubborn. I feel childish. And who are these people to tell me anything at all? *I should keep him, I'm a piece of shit and I'm going to hell, I should contact my local shelter and drop him off.* None of that's got shit to do with what I'd posted. It's a fucking rehoming ad, not an advice column. If I'd wanted to go about finding a shelter and dropping him off there, wouldn't I have done it? And if I was even considering keeping him, would I have posted the ad in the first place? Fucking useless, all of it. There was even somebody wanting to fly in from fucking Pittsburgh to come get him, and another guy was offering to pay *two hundred bucks* for the orange asshole? Is every single person in the fucking world on hardcore drugs?

I adjust my hat and try not to squirm in the uncomfortable seat. Grown men don't squirm. And I lock my hands together in front of me again. Matter-of-factly, I don't have a clue where the little bastard is, so their messages, well-intentioned and otherwise, were all for naught. Because among the insane number of responses to the rehoming ad had been a singular response to the equally insane number of job applications I'd filled out over the past week, and the email had indicated that the job interview was today, and in my panicked haste to get here on time, I'd only given the yard a cursory glance on my way out, and I'd seen nothing in the way of small and orange and psychotic.

And a part of me had felt relieved. And a part of me felt ashamed for feeling relieved. And still another part of me felt sad, oddly enough, but just as I start to inspect that earlier feeling of sadness a little closer-

"Misterrrrr…"

There's a man standing suddenly in front of me—a man so nondescript that I might not have noticed him if he hadn't placed himself

between me and the rays of sun blasting me in the face, what a noble sac-
rifice—and he's dragging that *r* out like it's my last name, Mr Rrrrrrr,
and even thought it only lasts a second or two, I feel like if he doesn't stop
soon, I'm gonna reach out and fucking—

"Gregory," I say blandly, standing up, and I suggest we shake hands
by offering my own, which I drag against my pants leg on the way up.

"Mr Gregory," he says proudly, like he's figured it out all his own.
He takes my hand and shakes it the way people do when they actually
enjoy meeting people. I'll be repulsed if he reaches out and hugs me, but
I won't be surprised. We sit down in unison. "So you're looking for a job?"

Part of me wants to ask why he'd ask me such a stupid question,
perhaps indicating myself, my current being, as if I'm for sale, because
things for sale always need to be indicated in some way. But instead I
say-

"Yep."

Another part of me wants to start talking and maybe never stop,
start talking about how hard it's been looking for a job with the impending
birth of my first child hanging over me like a piece of mistletoe—kiss
your ass goodbye, kiss the life you thought you knew goodbye—and how I
need a drink right now, because I always need a drink when life starts to
feel too real, and how I hate myself for needing the drink, and for a lot of
other shit, like having to be here, in this spot, both in time and in space,
on the corner of Rock Road and Bottom Boulevard, and-

"We do have a couple positions open." He looks at me critically, tilting
his head like a bird, perhaps trying to picture me mcflipping burgers,
mctaking orders, interacting with customers on a mcregular basis. "You
know, I think you'd be perfect for—"

A maintenance position, let me tell you what that entails, and I half-
listen to him and half-think about what I'd give to not have that ray of
sun drilling me in my left eye. *What it entails*: getting up at four a.m. and
riding a bicycle all the way here—well, fixing the bike first, making sure
Frank's capable of making the daily trip, fingers crossed—and working
until about eleven, and then riding my bike all the way back home, a

couple miles there, couple miles back. He says something about a certain amount of hours a week, and I nod and think about having enough
money to buy beer every night, having the money so I don't have to go
scrounging for loose pennies and aluminum cans to finance what always
turns out to be a relatively cheap trip to the corner store; and then I think
about having enough money to buy some diapers and wipes and formula
and toys or whatever, if only to make myself feel better about financially
prioritizing my drinking habit way of life.

"So d'you think this is something you'd be interested in?"

I nod and grimace cheerfully and say something about it sounding
perfect for me, and I ask if it's okay that my only mode of transportation
is a bicycle; and he says yeah, that's fine, and he says something about
other employees riding their bikes to work after school, and both of us
ignore the fact that I'll be twice as old as most of my coworkers. I ask him
about pay.

"Well, with this position, it'd be—"

I try not to laugh when he tells me the hourly rate, try not to get
up and walk out when I do some quick math and realize I might still be
scrounging for loose change and aluminum cans after all. I'm thinking
about how I'm gonna have to start sending rent out, because doesn't this
constitute getting back on one's feet? And how much of my net pay that'll
be, quite the chunk. I'm thinking about how few diapers and wipes and
formula and toys or whatever I'll actually be able to buy, and I'm thinking
about how little of it'll ultimately go toward drinking every night; and I
wonder, not so idly, if this short and modestly rounded and bespectacled
and otherwise nondescript man would say much of anything if I were to
just get up and walk the fuck out.

"Yeah, that'd be fine," my stupid lips say.

He nods agreeably and looks down at my application, cocking his
head to the side a bit. He really is quite birdlike. "You were in the military? Says here?"

I nod. "Army."

He's reading. "Deployed a couple times, says here?" Everything he says sounds like a question, but questions are safe, they don't require the same level of commitment as statements. "Fort Bragg...82nd Airborne Division...."

He trails off, appears to still be reading, but actually isn't. The sun is now burning the skin on my chin to a fine crisp. What he's really doing is what every interviewer to date has done, reading between the lines and thinking about all of the military movies they've seen—*Doesn't get any better than* Black Hawk Down, they'd say if you asked them—and picturing me doing those things, jumping outta airplanes and sliding down ropes and running with rifles and Being All I Can Be with the emotional capacity of an old boulder; and then thinking about me, that same person, taking out the garbage and flipping the occasional burger and cleaning out the restrooms and completing the most menial of tasks. Then his eyes scan a little lower, to the part where they'd asked if The Kid has ever been convicted of a felony, and where I'd put what they'd told me to put, the one piece of advice I'd been given before they put me in some civilian clothes and shoved me out the front—*Yes, would like opportunity to discuss further.* And I brace myself for it—*would you like tooooo*—and I'll lie and nod and say things that express an acceptance of responsibility and a very careful amount of regret, careful because if I say too much or show too much, I'm gonna end up showing him my bleeding fucking soul and how sorry I really am, which is not a careful amount at all, which is actually a very destructive amount, the sort of regret that shoves its way up into your sternum to where your heart is and grabs a big, bloody handful and squeezes so fucking tight, clenching the center of your very existence into fists made of fucking stone.

"I see," he says, nodding as though he really sees, smiling as though he really doesn't. "And when were you released from prison?"

I'm not sure I ever really was. "Coming up on a year."

"And this was down in North Carolina?"

I nod.

"No run-ins with the law since? No? And what about parole? No?"

I shake my head. "Finished a little while ago, actually, and I moved to this area right after."

He picks up the pile of papers in front of him and raps the edge against the table. It sounds like pool balls clicking. "So what made you decide to move up this way?"

I breathe a sigh of relief, inwardly anyway. An end is nigh. I say something about trying to finish writing a book, and he looks interested and asks what it's about, and I give him the very briefest of synopses— *it's basically about PTSD*. His interest seems genuine, but he doesn't really understand quite what it is he's interested about, so how genuine can it really be?

"And I have a baby on the way." I gesture at myself. "I mean, not me, personally." I figure it's a joke he'll like. He laughs. "So here I am."

My phone starts buzzing in my pocket. I wonder if he can hear it. It's pretty loud, or perhaps it seems loud to me because I can feel it, too. He looks down at the stack of papers in his hands, he's made them all neat, perhaps a reflection of the parallel tidying of his thoughts. "I believe in second chances," he says, and he looks for a moment like he's thinking about something he wishes he had a second chance at, like maybe he's about to tell me a story that will liken our lived experiences, but then he doesn't. "And I think you're a good kid, it's just...hard for me to picture you working here."

I wouldn't call myself comfortable, but I find myself at ease enough to smile. It feels real for once, but it's not a happy smile. It feels tired. I feel tired.

"I'm tired," I say. "I know that's not something I should say at a job interview." I gather a breath and exhale, ruffling the edges of his carefully stacked papers with depleted oxygen, and I find myself suddenly overwhelmed with fuck-it, the same sort of fuck-it that had probably led me to write that rehoming ad the way I did. "I'm overqualified, I know, I probably shouldn't be saying that either. And I'd be lying if I said I *truly* want to work here. I don't. But I'm here, and I'm here because I've been everywhere else, because I'm in no position to turn down even the smallest of opportunities. And I do need another chance at something, whatever that something is. I can't say I deserve it, but I do *need* it. And because I need it, I'll be here on time every morning, I'll work when and how much you want me to, and I'll even try to keep from bitching about it too much, that I'll throw in for free."

He looks a bit uncomfortable, as honesty is wont to make people, but he sees that I feel comfortable and tries to emulate, and succeeds a little bit, but fails a little bit. He nods, and some people walk by behind him, through the mcdining area filled with empty chairs, here for a late breakfast, or perhaps an early lunch, and they're looking at me weirdly, or I imagine they do, and I wonder exactly what I look like to them, big and bald and tattooed and very clearly applying for a job at a mcplace like this, a place good enough for them to eat, but not good enough for the mcworkers therein to receive any sort of respect, or like, a show of human decency or whatever.

And there's my phone buzzing again. That's two calls in a row. Nobody calls The Kid twice in a row, not even bill collectors. In my head, I picture Jessica, her roundness—*she's breathing a little hard from the effort, her cheeks flushed, her lips pursed around each belabored puff of air*—I mean, could it be?

"Well," he says amicably, and whether or not he's about to officially offer me the job remains to be seen, because I stand up then, too fast, and I'm sweating, although I may have been sweating the whole time, it feels like the fucking roof is on fire in here. I can't answer the phone in front of him, that's for sure on the list of Shit Not To Do At A Job Interview, and I'm still clinging to the hope that I might have actually landed myself some gainful employment. The interviewer—he says his name is Richard or something, and I try to remember if he's already told me that or not—he remains seated. I offer a quick apology—"But I've gotta take this call"—and a handshake, and Richard-or-something shakes my hand sitting down—which is quite odd, I don't know that I've ever shaken the hand of a seated man—and he says something about conferring with someone and asks if the phone number I wrote down is the correct number, and I say yes and reel my email off to him so he doesn't have to. Then he says something about being in touch and I say something about I hope so, and he laughs again, as I figured he would, and my phone's buzzing again—that's three calls in a row, back-to-back-to-*back*—so I toss him a quick smile, and I stride through the now-not-so-empty dining room, past the late-breakfasters and early-lunchers, and I step through the door and answer—it's Emily—my eyes squinting in the brightness, breathing in deep all the reds and oranges and yellows I couldn't from inside, and I turn a relieved face into the wind, toward the soft breeze moving through, and my heart feels like it's gonna just fucking explode right along with my right eardrum as the world's longest iteration of the word *time* pierces my eardrum like a flaming arrow.

CHAPTER SIXTEEN

The streets are teeming with a post-lunch haste, a blanket of slowly moving cars buzzing with reserved impatience. The sounds of people being late. Stress-lined faces, white-knuckling steering wheels, tight-lipped smiles upon eye contact. Sunlight booms down from above, bounces off blacktop, car tops, bald heads, and everything moves and then stops and then moves again, lines of cars slinking through the hot streets like a greased grub. Wes, her fiancé of 600 years, is driving, Emily having deemed herself unfit to operate a motor vehicle at this time, but the only thing she's drunk on is anxiety, the preferred pick of poison among America's young adults. He adds his car horn to the mix of those blaring and beeping and tooting. It's more of a habit thing than anything else. No one lays on the horn thinking it's going to affect the flow of traffic. It's just something one does.

You're going to be a daddy. To a little girl. It's real, it's going to be very fucking real. And it's either step up or step out, no pussyfooting around, no one leg in and one leg out like you're doing the hokey-pokey, but you had better turn yourself around, because you're at wits' end with a fucking KITTEN I mean just look at yourself a KITTEN is giving you fits he's got you—

"The fucking kitten," I whisper, and I tack on a couple extra swear words for good measure, because there's no such thing as too much colorful language when it comes to that little cabbagehead. "*Shit.*"

"What?" Emily asks from the front passenger seat.

"Nothing," I say, because what am I *supposed* say, that I'm cursing myself for being a miserable wretch once again? That I put the little bastard on the stoop last night without a second thought for it until it was too late, until I'd already done it and been done with it? That I'd *apparently* penned a glorious rehoming ad to commemorate what a giant fuckwhistle he is, and then gone to bed after that, drunken and prone to misremembering come the morning after, and that I hadn't seen a single whisker of the little shitter since?

"How's that kitten doing?"

"He's doing," I say, and leave it at that. Because what am I *supposed* to say?

I'm spared any further inquisition, for the moment at least, because the traffic does move, is moving, and after a nerve-rackingly short while, shaves our car off into the hospital parking lot, a shred of cheese breaking off from the block by way of grater. As is the way with such things, there are exactly zero parking spots to be had within screaming distance of the entrance.

"Go, just go, we'll park and come in after," Emily says. Wes nods in agreement, but he's already peering up the row of cars glinting in front of him, looking for somewhere to park. I don't know who's more anxious, Emily or me, but it feels neck and neck.

"Are you sure you don't wanna go in for me?" I feel like if I step out of the car and start walking toward the hospital entrance, everything's gonna start melting, each step getting harder and harder to pull back up, the world is a big, nasty fucking tar pit, and then the buildings will start to go, withering away from the bottom up, huge chunks of this reality cascading down on me in pale, gray, lukewarm globs. And on the other side, who knows, maybe I'm still sprinting across some thankless piece of dried earth in Samarra, I'm chasing some scared kid down because he's just old enough to be deemed a threat and tackling him and dragging his hands behind him, securing them with a zip tie while he pleads with me in a language I don't understand; or standing in the courtroom again, my heart feels as if someone violent and cold has reached into my chest and clenched it tight, and his family is standing behind me, I can hear his mother crying and his brother consoling, and the only thing I want is to turn around and drop to my knees and plead for a forgiveness I know I don't deserve; or sitting in a concrete tomb for the thousand-and-some-thingth day, I've lost myself, I no longer know who I am except for this, 1282263, because I've replaced life's tangibility with memories of past tangible shit and dreams of future tangible shit and doing otherwise leaves one to reflect on the floaty, very intangible existence one inherits upon being stripped of one's real name in favor of another, courtesy of the North Carolina Prison System.

"Go," she says, and it's less anxious this time, gentler. So I go.

The pavement crunches beneath my shoes as I walk, asphalt covered with a gritty mix of dirt and loose gravel. The thornless stem of a pink rose creases the palm of my left hand, nothing but cold sweat in the right, and I begin to pass people leaving, people arriving, and suddenly I'm through the doors and halfway to the receiving desk of the maternity ward. The woman behind the desk peers at me as I approach, stopping on a dime just in front of her. Her eyes are magnified by thick glasses, and her hair is a flyaway tumbleweed only just corralled by a hurried morning routine. Her chin, I notice, crumples back against her neck, pale and sharply cornered, and reminds me of a poorly made paper airplane.

"I'm here to see my daughter?" The sort of uncertainty that turns statements into questions.

"Name, sir?"

"Mine? My name?"

"Not yours, sir. The mother's." Her voice sounds like she chews a lot of gum with her mouth open, smacking and disdainful. I tell her the name.

"Okay, room 428."

"That's on the fourth floor?"

She peers up at me again, as if seeing me for the first time, or as if to commit my face and this interaction to memory for later, when she'll get home a little too late to catch her boyfriend of over seven years leaving for his shift at SMS, where he makes $11.38 an hour for ten or twelve hours at a time, which, in his humble opinion, is very worth getting away from her and the hitherto unspoken commitment she really wants and he really doesn't. She'll call her sister then, or Skype maybe, and they'll drink cheap wine together, Franzia, and she'll cry without crying about how said boyfriend doesn't really see her anymore, and her sister will console her, and pat her on the back from hundreds of miles away, and after a few glasses, things will seem better and the conversation will turn to the guy she dealt with at work today, this Idiot, who needed help figuring out that the first digit of the room number corresponds with the floor on which the room is located. And then, you know, they will laugh, a derisive sort of unhappiness made otherwise, at least momentarily, by

Sunset Blush, a delicate pink hue boasting such merits as *Strawberry Flavors* and *Easy to Drink* and *Very Refreshing*.

"Yeah," she says, bored, looking back down at the magazine on the desk in front of her. "Yeah, fourth floor."

I spin away from her before the last of this leaves her lips, an abrupt left-face, and walk to the bay of elevators. The floor is lustrously antiseptic and squeaks beneath my shoes, loudly, but I hear them as if from underwater. I'm conscious of my heart, its tangible existence, now moreso than ever. It's thumping painfully against my breastbone, and my breath, comparatively and congruently, is shallow and coarse and dry and, actually, not unlike the old man standing just to my right and rear, teetering his balance from one point of his tripodal base to the other, seemingly without warning or cause, the random quick ticks of a broken clock. He reaches with his cane, a dangerous maneuver, and jabs it at the button indicating one's desire to Go Up. I nod thanks and go through the act of smiling, falsely quirking nervous lips, he sees none of this, and I grip the rose tighter.

The doors ding.

They open.

And we enter.

The fourth floor is dimmer, whether by design or electrical wiring malfunction. The lighting is fleshy and almost velutinous and reflects the floor's waxed surface up at me as I walk, my throat ever drier, my shirt affecting dark and rebellious circles at the pits. I receive permission to proceed from the fourth-floor equivalent of the bespectacled counterpart below and squeak my way down the hall. I whisper the room numbers to myself as I go, as if verbalizing in some way ensures I won't miss the one I'm looking for. They're segregated, odds to the left and evens to the right, and I watch them, walking, squeaking, whispering—

"Four-twenty-four. Four-twenty-six. Four-twenty—"

Four-twenty-eight. It's a regular door, not special. The handle, a plain stainless steel, is also very unspecial, and suddenly, the unremark-ableness of it all hits me, how plain it is, how routine and ordinary and so actual that it belies not only the entire process up until now, but also the neoteric phenomenon lying behind its plain plainness. But I clear my throat of dust anyway, and I wipe my free hand dry anyway, on my pants, and I grab the door handle, cool and sterile and very plain, and I push the door open anyway, entering, and—

The problem with The Kid is that, for all of his Running Away, he's gone nowhere. The point of Running Away is either to get toward or get away, but The Kid just been jogging in fucking place, or like, trying to get away and calling it getting toward, and were he to look behind him at any given moment—and he does, boy, does he—he'd see that the ghosts of his past are right there, ever present, watching almost, and waiting for him, The Kid, to slip up, when they'll gather ever closer to him and hover in hungry circles like vultures just above the withered cage that houses his bleeding fucking soul, tearing off pieces of The Kid in chunks for themselves. He'd never really left that house on West Jackson, had he, because it had taken something from of him, something dear and personal, and that piece was still there. And his tours overseas had kept a piece of him, and so had August 14, 2010, and so had the justified aftermath, his imprisonment, all of these ghosts ripping off chunks of The Kid for themselves, and then following close behind as he Runs Away some more, moving skeletally, just in case he slips up again. Because he always does.

Boy, does *he.*

Her eyes are deep and dark. Paper-thin eyelids lined with lashes the color of spilt ink, they flick and flutter like moth wings. Intricate designs scrawled across her tiny palms, as if she'd grabbed a spiderweb wet with spring dew. Her skin is smoother than glass. I drag a rough thumb across her cheek. She winces.

"What do you think?"

I look up. The bed looks uncomfortable. She doesn't, she's fucking *glowing*, if anything. She smiles. I smile back. "She's uh—" I look back down at the warm bundle lying on my lap. "I dunno what to say."

"Understandable."

"Are you okay, how are you feeling?"

"Tired. Exhausted, actually. But it went a lot smoother than I was anticipating. She kinda just...shot right outta there."

I snort. "Good thing the doctor caught her, I reckon." She laughs lightly. I look back down at the baby, she's wrapped her fingers around one of mine, she's clenching in a way that makes me feel...*wanted* or something. No, *needed* or something, and it's a feeling to which I'm not very accustomed. Not as of late. Not as of ever, really. But it's not quite the feeling I was expecting. "Is she healthy?"

"Very healthy."

"No problems at all?"

"None. I don't think it could've gone much more..."

Perfectly, she's gonna say perfectly and then she doesn't, because we're not just two parents quietly discussing the much-anticipated arrival of a beautiful baby. Things are realer than that, and what's real is that I should've been there and perhaps I'd know how it went. What's real is that everything I've done over the past year has done little to suggest I'm ready for this, and hell, I don't feel ready right now and it's already happened. And what's really fucking real is that I've done nothing to deserve the right to be here right now, she's got every reason in the world to keep me away, to ask that I get help for the shit that ails me before being allowed to see the baby, but she hadn't, oh *contraire mon frere*, she'd even tracked me down—on the eve of childbirth, no less—to offer me the opportunity to be here for this, an opportunity for things to go perfectly for real, and I'd dropped the fucking ball on that one, hadn't I?

"Thank you," I say. "For calling Emily. And allowing me to be here. I—"

Speak of the devil and she shall appear. Emily bursts through the door, buzzes into the room like a June bug, and she's crooning something in a language I don't recognize, something with lots of Bs and Ws. She extends her arms as if I've torn the baby from her own breast, and I hand the baby over, feeling a little relieved as I swallow what was going to be yet another apology. Her sudden arrival also prevents Jessica from having to act like she believes me this time.

Because isn't this where it's supposed to happen? Coming through the door, seeing that little baby, everything moving slowly and gently, almost as if the guy's being born himself, fucking reborn, and it's gotta happen, it better, and if this or something like this doesn't happen, well, the guy's not ready, he's not cut out to be a father, might as well pack it up and pack it in, hit the fucking road, toss a dart at the map, who fucking cares where. Go west, young man, isn't that what our old pal Horace said? Fuck it, go east, go south, go north, go anywhere, just get away, Run Away, because something special was supposed to happen inside of you—like the rays of a rising sun booming through thin, white curtains, the reflection of a summer moon on gently chattering water, the way a first kiss tastes when the football game is over and the boys are all sweaty and the girls are all giggly and there's kids running around on the field, they're tossing a ball back and forth and pretending for a moment that they're their big brothers, and things aren't packed up, but are being packed up, and there's just enough time to dip beneath the bleachers and tug on her hand and melt into her as she melts into you and ignore the distant calls of your friends, the way losing the game tonight made you feel, as you press your lips against hers in the dark and pray, oh *pray*, that you're not fucking this up—and it hadn't, the moment just hadn't happened.

The general hubbub caused by Emily's arrival gives me the opportunity to phase out of the room like a ghost. The hallway is brighter than the room, seemingly brighter than I remember, and cold. Or actually, not cold, but my hands are fucking freezing, so I bury them in my pockets and hunch my shoulders up around my ears like a man stepping out onto his porch first thing in the morning, huffing on a cigarette and trying to determine whether or not it's warm enough to leave his jacket at home today. A nurse comes out of a room a couple doors up, she's pushing some hulking piece of equipment out in front of her, and I feel out of place, like maybe she should call security or grab a sponge and some cleaner and come scrub me off the wall like the stain I am. She smiles at me. I try to smile back, and grimace instead, *now that wasn't a very good smile at all, now was it?*

"Are you okay?"

I almost fall out of my skin, and I turn around. Jessica's standing just outside the door in socks and a barely-there hospital gown. "Where's the baby, shouldn't we—"

"Emily has Luna, she's fine."

I nod an okay. "But shouldn't you be in bed or something. I bet you're tired."

She cocks her head a little and smiles and says, "Well yeah, I guess I am a little tired after all," and I smile at the light sarcasm—*of course she's tired, you dolt*—because I know she's messing with me, and then everything seems a little bit more okay.

"So what do you think?"

"I think...I don't know what to think."

"It can be overwhelming." She checks my expression. "It can also be very underwhelming."

I nod.

She says, "You've probably thought about this moment for a long time. It's normal, don't worry."

"I think I'm just...I dunno. All you ever hear about is this bolt-of-lighting realization, and you're a dad in that moment, everything comes together and falls into place, and you don't really have to worry about it because it's natural, you see, carnal, primal, whatever, and—"

She raises an eyebrow. "That's the way it works, eh?"

I shrug. "Isn't it?"

She sighs. "No, of course that's not how it fucking works. Whatever you're feeling now, whether it be over- or underwhelming, it's something you'll add to each time you see her. And not feeling something isn't indicative of what sort of dad you'll be, any more than feeling something is. Just think of it as a beginning. And think of yourself as in control of that beginning. And one day, you'll realize that everything has come together, everything has fallen into place, and not because it's just supposed to, but because you took control and made it happen."

Soft chatter from the nurses' station comes floating down the hallway. Babies crying in other rooms. Mothers soothing. EKGs beeping responsibly. I hear the ding of the elevator, the doors jolting and sliding open, the sound of murmured excuse-mes, the shuffling of careful feet and murmured instructions to keep those feet careful. Someone laughs. I think I hear soft sobbing a little ways down. I don't wanna think about that. Sneakers squeak on polished floors. There are two exits, I wonder which is closer, definitely the one to my right, the letters are the red of diluted blood.

"So now what," I say, shrugging in spite of myself, reflexive.

"I don't know," she says, adding a lightly sarcastic shrug of her own. "I was gonna ask you the same thing."

CHAPTER SEVENTEEN

Oh, and what did you ever do about that crazy kitten?

I'm sitting on the stoop again, just call me Stoop Kid, with a lukewarm beer in one hand and my phone in the other, the latter of which is buzzing at annoyingly close intervals, but my eyes are farther away, out across the road and the field to the train tracks, and my mind is even farther away than that, out across an incalculable distance of time and space, where I sit and ponder the complete lack of feeling I'd had upon seeing my daughter, Luna Rae, for the first time.

No, not a complete lack—shock, perhaps; awe, an overpowering sense of dumbfoundedness; but that'd been it, there'd been no bolt of lightning come down to zap me in the ass, no sudden epiphany and resulting turn-around. I was fucking taken aback, and then it was over, and two minutes after we'd gotten into the roasting car and driven away, it'd been as if it'd never happened, as if it simply couldn't *have—*

The sun has set, but it's not dark out. Tired rays peek above the horizon, clinging to the day. I raise the almost-full can to my lips, and I slurp, my nose prickling with the smell of carbonated hops. It's warm beer, but it's *a* beer, and beggars can't be choosers.

Emily and Wes had dropped me off back home afterward, Emily giving me a hug that felt like we were returning from a funeral, perhaps meaning to be comforting, and she'd whispered in my ear in a creepy way, perhaps meant to be conspiratorial, and she'd asked me, as she had so many fucking times over the last year, if I was alright, do I need money, or like, *anything*? And I'd detached myself from her as gently as possible, and I'd said that I was fine, that maybe I even had a job, I'd have to wait and see, but that I'd seen a case of newly minted Bud Lights on the backseat floor, and that a thirsty man—i.e. me—would be in no position to turn down a few of them, were she to offer, of course.

I take another slurp, and most of the can follows behind. My phone buzzes again, and again. I sigh.

She had given me a look, but hadn't said anything, just reached into the backseat and handpicked a few of the forbidden fruit, just for me, and handed them over with this fucking *look* on her face, like a drug dealer with a sudden attack of conscience for the disease-ridden addict, and I'd taken them from her with the meekness of the latter, and just stood there as they said some goodbyes and backed out of the driveway, and they'd waved, and I'd waved back, beers in both hands, but I'd waved back, and I just stood there as the back of their car dwindled to a point down the long, rural road, my heart sinking at the same pace, and the silence they'd left behind had gone on way too long when I punctuated the happenings of the day with a loud *sssssk-pop* that frightened a sleeping squirrel just overhead into a long-winded scolding that had lasted exactly two beers.

My phone vibrates again. It's either I'm *a piece of shit* or I *should keep him*, I'd bet fucking money on it, but since we're on the topic of money, I guess there's a chance one of the annoying buzzings had been an email notifying me of my new mcjob, and if I could say one more thing about money, it'd be about how much I *don't* have and how much I *do* need, and *maybe* I'm not in a position to be ignoring these notifications, because *maybe*—

I push myself up off the stoop and chuck the wretched rectangle out into the yard, where it bounces like a wayward golf ball, because *fuck* it, and because I don't have time for the *bullshit* tonight, because I'm some-baby's *daddy*, you hear me, somebaby's *father,* and everything else can wait until tomorrow morning, when I'll wake up with a pounding head and a dry mouth and probably some regrets.

Because aren't there always some regrets?

I polish off the beer and crack open another one—the squirrel's fucked off somewhere over the rainbow, thank god—and I set off across the yard, cutting down the side of the house running parallel to the ditch and squeezing past a very large tree on a very small piece of grass, holding onto my beer and a prayer as I try to keep myself from keeling over into the squeaking tufts of ditch weeds; and I make it, and I continue on into the backyard, my eyes peeled for anything that might hint at the whereabouts of the kitten that was apparently in high demand, thanks to my drunken typing the night before, because the next time I check my phone, it'll be with kitten in hand, ready to be rehomed, ready to fuck off over the rainbow himself, in exchange for one last influx of cash, of course—i.e. *that'll be twenty-five doll hairs, my friend, and cya-cya, wouldn't wanna be ya*—and that might just be enough to get me by until something develops fucking *something*, fucking *anything*.

"Uuuuh, CMEREKITTY," I bellow. I take a drink of beer, and harken back to the ad I'd written about the bastard, what had I called him. "Uuuuh, CMEREDITCHKITTY!"

Nothing. Maybe the neighbor peeking through his blinds, as if his fucking name is Cmereditchkitty Smith, but otherwise—nothing.

—you're at wits' end with a fucking KITTEN I mean just look at yourself a KITTEN is giving you fits—

"Fuck," I sigh. The beer has me feeling warm and optimistic, but it's still early in the night. "CMERE, DITCH!"

More nothingness. More drinks of beer. I think about flipping off the tiny slit in the neighbor's blinds, and I'm halfway there when it occurs to me that it might be just that, a tiny slit in the neighbor's blinds, and nothing else, *you paranoid fuck.* And it's getting dark, actually *is* dark now, so I hop the fence separating the backyard from the ditch—some sort of something still squeaking down there, probably something fucking rabid—and I enter the house through the backdoor, finishing my next-to-last beer and tossing the empty can down into the basement with perfect form, and I pull my last one out of my back pocket, last beer of the night, and I crack it and take a dainty sip as I walk into the living room and sit down at my desk.

"Maybe something to tide them over," I mutter, and I open my computer and click my way to Craigslist, where I select the option to edit the rehoming ad that had garnered so much interest in the little fuckwhistle. *I'll find him. How far could he have gone?* "Just something to tide them over..."

~

SOMEONE PLEASE COME ADOPT THIS ASSHOLE (BAY CITY)

UPDATE: Those of you who have expressed interest in this asshole, I apologize for the delay in responding to your emails. I never expected this demonic little shit to garner so much attention, and I'm doing my best to weed through the emails and find the best place for him, one where he'll get all the cheese popcorn his heart desires. Thank you for your patience, and here are a few more pictures of Ditch for your viewing pleasure. I know he's cute, but do not be fooled. My wallet is missing, and I know he had something to do with it.

So The Kid stamps the gas with his foot and hangs onto the brake for dear life, the back tires begin to wail and scream, obnoxiousness and arrogance and youth, perhaps all interchangeable, perhaps basically the same. The back end of the truck yaws left and then right, port and starboard, threatening to clip the side of this car, surprise-surprise, this Mustang. There's a song leaking from The Kid's speakers, something about being famous, something about moving forward and breaking through, and the lyrics, although sorta hard to hear, they're dirty and grated and hot brass bouncing off slick skin, touching and sticking and burning for a moment before ricocheting off, a myriad of death rattles, and The Kid turns it up, I mean, turns it the fuck *up. There's no such thing as music too loud in this moment, no such thing as too much laughter or too fast or this costs too much money, this is too dangerous, this is—*

The truck explodes out of the intersection, through the intersection, onward, rocketing through the night like the proverbial bat, tires screaming and music screaming and a couple screams of laughter, of excited joy. The Kid straddles the center line, bright yellow streaks flashing beneath the truck at the speed of light, nay, even faster. The Kid tries to crank the tunes a little louder, but it's maxed out, everything's maxed out. The scent of midsummer blasts in through the windows, creeping beneath the sleeve of his shirt and flapping it against his arm like a crisp flag. This is how The Kid learned to drive, never touched the steering wheel of a car until he was eighteen and in Iraq and somebody asked him hey, you know how to drive, right? *And of course The Kid says yes and strides to the Humvee with confidence and stuffs himself into the driver's seat, pulls hard on the heavy door and crams himself and his equipment behind the wheel. And The Kid had learned real fast that most driving done in a warzone is done under duress, is done with The Kid sweating his fucking balls off in a hundred and fifty pounds of gear and hot air blasting him in the face and a set of NVGs attached to his head. He learns on the run, on the drive, and hell yeah he makes mistakes, I mean, who the fuck drives under NVGs, who the fuck does sixty mph in the middle of the night with the very real threat of an IED blasting you to fuck and back—sixty on the highway, sixty through tiny streets lined with sleeping houses but very awake people, sixty in the tracks of the Humvee in front of you—hurtling through a warzone with nothing but a general disregard for your own life and a prayer? Who fucking does that?*

The Kid's getting all sorts of support from the backseat, typical of backseaters, but there's not much naysaying, and then there's a corner. The Kid thinks about slowing down, but it's not a very intimidating corner, it's not a sharp turn that maybe requires a bit of finesse and a bit of brakes, a bit of caution, and so The Kid hits it at 60. It's too sharp. And a deep hush falls over the world. For just a moment, there's no music and roaring tailpipes and screaming tires. There's no laughter or smiles, no mirth. The truck hits the turn hard enough to go airborne, hard enough to lift it into the air a bit, the back end pulling away from the turn, the front end in cahoots with it. The truck hits the ground again, but it hits on two wheels instead of four, the starboard side lifting. For a second, everything hangs in the balance, whichever balance that is, eyes wide, mouths agape, hearts stopped. And then the truck manages to right itself, all four tires thumping to the road with little to no grace, and everything comes back, the loud music and the pipes roaring with excited anger and, although perhaps a bit late to the party, the laughter, one's feeling of invincibility, one's overall sense of self and life and well-being. And the smell of beer and whiskey fills the truck, ridding the air of that momentary clarity.

And then there's another intersection—The Kid slows down just enough to take this particular turn without flipping the truck—and although he doesn't know it, it's the last turn he'll make in this truck, the last time he'll stomp on the gas and feel his back pressing into his seat, the last time he'll rocket down any road at all. It's the last time he'll feel like he's traveling at the speed of fucking light. It's the last time he'll look ahead to the next intersection and see a distant traffic light, a blurry pin-

prick in the night, swaying in the summer breeze, balancing itself upon invisible waves like a buoy, like a dark ship set adrift on dark waters, with nothing but that single, blinking red light to indicate its—

A van skips out into the street with a wiggle and a shimmy, settling into the lane right in front of The Kid as he blows through the intersection, and suddenly where there was once nothing is now the wide ass-end of a beaten minivan, there's so much detail, the dust-encrusted back window, at least one bumper sticker attesting something, maybe there's two, and black taillights and the grumbling toot of exhaust, and The Kid jerks and twists the steering wheel, an overconfident swerve, and the music disappears, and the sounds of carefree laughter and the engine roaring and angry tailpipes, everything dissipates, and all that's left is the ugly, panicked sound of tires battling the truck's inertia, the inertia of too many bad decisions in a row, an act perpetrated by whom, by him, by The Kid.

No.

By me. By fucking me.

I feel like time is supposed to stop, slow or something, but it doesn't. The universe turns its back as I snatch the wheel to the left, jerking the nose of the truck away from imminent impact, and the sharp swerve throws the truck into a violent fishtail. All I can hear now is screaming, tires screaming against pavement, voices screaming ohmygod *and* watchout-watchout. *The palms of my hands are gripping the steering wheel too tight and I'm wrenching it, all of it, as hard left as I can, away from the van, out of the current lane and into the one running parallel, the turn lane, a lane occupied by a single headlight, a motorcycle I haven't seen until only just now, and—*

And this is where it happens. This is where a mass of bad decisions culminates in something dark and terrible, where the world erupts into a din of shrieking metal and shattering glass and screams, my god, the screaming. *The truck doesn't come to a stop, it hits the motorcycle and ricochets away, fishtailing so violently I'm almost certain it's going to rip in half, dumping us into the road like kicked Barbies. I'm blinking through the spray of powderized glass hitting me in the face, stomping the brakes through the floor before I remember and let off, wrangling the truck to stop, the front tires slamming into the curb hard enough to chip teeth. Everything falls silent then, a deathly quiet, the panicked breathings of someone close enough to Death to feel His cold fingers caressing one's face, the throaty cough of the truck's engine struggling to recover. Lauren begins to squeak then, I think she's trying to cry, squeaking like a mouse what's been stepped on, and I have to get away from it, I have to go, I have to continue on and get on with my life and forget this ever happened, and that way, I think, this will have never happened, the past does not exist, the future does not exist, there is only the present, and in the present, I find myself grabbing the steering wheel again, testing the gas a little, ignoring the tears rolling down my face because I've gotta go, I've gotta—*

Go, you need to go, *someone says from the back seat, short of breath, panicky.* You need to go, YOU NEED TO—

Perhaps it's the voice's too-urgent tone, perhaps it's my own ugliness reflected in the mirror of those words, but I stop. And I sit there. Stunned into silence. Things like this always happen to Someone Else, never you, never me, always him and her and them and Someone Else. The truck is resting against the curb like a kicked can, don't forget to recycle. The engine coughs and mutters to a stop. There's smoke billowing from the front, maybe it's steam, leaking through the mangled remains of the grill in tendrils, reaching toward the heavens unassumingly.

GO, *the voice from the backseat says, almost pleading with me, but I don't.* CMON GO, *the voice says, but I can't. There's something dark and terrible out there, the fruits of my own horrible labor, and I've gotta face it, I've gotta uncurl my fingers from the steering wheel, I've gotta shove the damaged remains of the driver-side door open and get out, not away, but OUT.*

I push the door open and fall into the street. There's glass everywhere, there's blood and glass everywhere. It's hot, the air is hot, the pavement and the truck, I'm sweating, it's all hot, too hot. I think I can hear sirens rising in the distance, but there's no way, it's too soon. Isn't it? Because I've got no concept of time, I cannot fathom how it continues to move, why the world doesn't just stop, how the seconds continue to tick-tick-tick. I want everything to stop, but not just stop, I need it to rewind, and I find myself climbing to my feet now, turning my face toward what's left of the motorcycle, toward the intersection, toward the body lying in the middle of it all, toward—

Please, *I whisper, taking a step, a couple steps.* Please don't be—

But hands are laid upon my person, arms holding me back and pulling me away, dragging me out of the road, away from what remains, what remains of his night and mine, his life and mine. I fight against them, trying to push toward the intersection, because everything is gonna be fine, I mean, a mistake was made, but I can make it right, The Kid can make it right if they'd just let him get close enough. But they succeed in restraining me and I'm sat down on the curb, my legs straight out in front of me, everything beginning to blur together, everything blending and becoming a mass of nothing, and the sirens pick up then, small and distant, minute and far away, blurry pinpricks in the night, but rising and rising, closer and closer, and I just sit there, limp, my arms hanging by my side like cold slabs of pork, the back of my wrists touching the pavement, my head hanging as I hope, as I pray to a god I don't believe in, asking him/her/it to make all of this okay, to make sure the motorcyclist is okay, even as a smattering of people gather somberly around the body lying in the intersection, even as one of them shakes his heads sadly, and so does another, and they turn to look at me with the beginnings of what feels like venom in their gaze, even as the sirens grow closer and closer, even as the other occupants of my truck gather around me, shushing my rising panic, blocking the intersection from view and telling me that everything's gonna be okay, but it doesn't make me feel any better. It makes me feel a deep disgust that I haven't felt since black widows, genus latrodectus, found throughout much of the world, *because this is not something that's happened to me, it's something I've done.*

Please, *I whisper, beginning to rock back and forth.* Please let him be okay, please.

Please.

Please.

CHAPTER EIGHTEEN

I jolt awake so hard I almost fall out of bed, only just catching myself on the nightstand, my arm shooting out like a well-greased kick-stand, and I'm awake, am I not, I'm awake and everything is okay, temporarily, and I sit there in a dark for a bit, wiping away the mixture of sweat and tears pouring down my face. The nightmare clings to me like goo. Sticking to me. Refusing to let go. I can feel the sheets bunched up beneath me, rolled into a makeshift ball from my tossing and turning, and everything feels damp, the bed, the pillow lying askew beneath my head, the air. I reach up and behind me to open the window, it's already cracked a bit, so I shove it as open as it'll go, breathing in deeply, the chilly night air pricking my skin with the feeling of thousands of ants' feet marching. The air feels heavy, pregnant, as if there's a very big something just overhead, and right on cue, I hear the distant rush of rain dashing across the cornfields. Car tires whine wetly in the distance, approaching, buzzing, ever nearer, ever closer, and then suddenly here and then just as suddenly not, driving away, ever onward. And I can still hear the sirens that pervaded my dreams, screaming, screaming, and I fall back into it for a moment, the nightmare, awake but not, half in and half out, back there at the intersection of Murchison and Country Club, where the latter turns into Pamalee, with the screaming, the screaming, and the careless wreckage, the carpet of shattered glass, and *I find myself climbing to my feet now, turning my face toward what's left of the motorcycle, toward the intersection, toward the—*

My phone buzzes, I think, and I jolt awake and paw at the darkness, but it's not on the nightstand—either that or it'd buzzed itself off into the abyss—and now I'm leaning over the edge of the bed for it, my dangling hand sweeping across the carpet—the sound of rustling clothes, crinkled aluminum cans tinking emptily—and it's only once I begin to slide ever so slowly out of bed that I remember chucking my phone out into the yard like a fucking moron; and I just give up then, slide completely to the floor and just lay there amidst the rustled clothes and empty cans, drunk and defeated and in dire need of something, anything at all, that might deliver me from this hell.

Another beer might do the trick.

So I'm up then, out the door to the hallway, through the living room and into the dark peacefulness of the kitchen. The rain smacks against the window, it sounds like pocketed marbles. I pull the fridge open, but it's empty, save a bottle of mustard, save a piece of cheese, because I'd drank what Emily had given me, and that had been it, there was no more, and might not be anytime soon.

Look at me, still drinking, still making poor choices. She's got a firm hold on me, this drunkenness, this inability to abstain, the failed drowning of memories and choices and memories of choices and et cetera, the fucking firmest of holds.

I slam the fridge shut and step to the sink. The rain seems to pick up as I get closer to the window. I turn the water on and splash a cupped handful into my face, once and again, and a drink a couple handfuls, too, washing the taste of sleep from my mouth, and it's only once I begin to taste salt that I realize I'm still fucking *crying*.

"*Fuck!*" I say, and I shut the water off and raise my shirt to wipe my face, trying to scrub away the weakness.

Nothing changed. And that's the problem. Because I waited for things to change, as if change is inevitable, because it is, isn't it? But inevitable change is not the same as accepting change and causing change and making change. And waiting around for stuff to just happen because it eventually must, what sort of life is that?

I walk back through the house to the bathroom, where I piss and then splash my face with more water, and I stare at myself blearily in the mirror too long, inspecting the lines in my face for genuineness, as if I doubt my own sadness, as if the sorrow I feel can't possibly be real, because I'm the one who did it, and what right do I have to be full of sorrow for something that never would have fucking happened if not for *me*?

But I am. I can't help it. I feel sad about it all the time, sometimes so much so that the pain is almost unbearable, so much so that I just want to fucking *die—a voluntary kicking of the fucking bucket or whatever*—but if I couldn't do it before, if I couldn't find the courage to just end it before ever meeting Luna, then where was I gonna find the goddamn gumption *now*?

"Funny way to say she's giving you a reason to live," I say to myself in the mirror, watching my lips move, watching my eyes flick down to watch my lips move. "Full of fucking epiphanies tonight, aren't we?" I stretch my lips back and bare my teeth as I add a few extra syllables to the last word.

But maybe that's what change needs sometimes—not *inevitable* change, *making* change—maybe that's something The Kid could've used, eh, a couple of epiphanies, a fucking lightbulb or something, and maybe then he'd I'd have realized that there were some things in my life that needed some serious fucking changing, same as right now, assuming I have plans to step *up* instead of *out,* assuming I have plans to actually be a parent, to stick around instead of leaving, instead of Running Away again, instead of perpetuating the fucking cycle.

—are you the sorta guy who can take care of something and be gentle for once and not just gentle with your hands but with your heart too and—

—you're at wits' end with a fucking KITTEN—

—you should keep—

—it might help you to feel less alone—

"Oh, *shit*." The damn kitten.

Here's your chance to make *change instead of* waiting *for it,* I think to myself only a little sarcastically, and I hear the storm pick up outside as I walk across the cranky floor to the front, the rain smacking against the windows, and I stuff bare feet into boots and unlock the door, and I pull it open, flicking the porch light on and bracing myself against the steadily rising storm as I peer out into an impenetrable nothingness fraught with gusts of cold wind that sound like screaming women and pellets of rain sheeting down like dropped needles.

—he's nervous, his hands shaking, and he can feel her body curling up toward his finger, dangling there like a rancid grape, her seven other legs wrapping around the tip and dangling there cancerously, her maw shining and sticky and flexing—

"Cmere, Cat!" I call out. The wind snatches my words like a thief. I step off the stoop—a great feat for Stoop Kid—and I walk gingerly out into the yard, into the nothingness. "Cmere kitty, cmere Ditch!"

He doesn't cmere, but I'm not surprised, I hadn't really expected him to. I strain my eyes against the darkness, trying to keep them open against the hard rain, and I shade them with a flat hand, and I peer harder.

—he looks through his own sights in the direction of the pointed finger, blinking a couple times, salty eyelashes and dry eyes, and fixes the red dot on the windshield of an approaching car—

I take a couple more steps, first toward the road, and I veer left sharply—half because I'm still fucking drunk, half because I see something glinting in the grass closer to the ditch, something reflecting the thick grays overhead and the meager light shining palely above the stoop—and I hiss some cmere-kitties into the night, but the reflecty thingy doesn't move, because of course it doesn't move, because of course it's just the phone I'd yeeted out into the yard earlier—and I pick it up, and I kick at the tree closest to the ditch running perpendicular to the street, like he's going to fucking fall out of it or something, I dunno, but what else is there to do? I can't see a fucking thing, nor can I hear a fucking thing above the storm raging around me, above the rain hitting and the trees rustling and snapping like they're on fire and the wind moaning around the corners of the house, the sound of widows keening over heavy caskets. I'm soaked and freezing and pissed and cussing up a storm bigger than the one around me, and tired, too, ready to throw in the towel, and go inside and get a towel. I'd tried to *make change*, hadn't I? And for nothing, The Kid would have to just chalk it up to the game, just something else to keep me awake at night, something else to add to a long list of fuck-ups, and for *what*, and for fucking *nothing*, I hadn't wanted the fucker anyway, from the very beginning, and shit, maybe this is it, maybe it's *not* another fuck-up, maybe it's a *boon*, hell, and maybe he'd wanted to go just as much as I wanted him to go, and maybe this was just him going in his own way, and not being rehomed, shuffled off to live with somebody who would touch him too much and talk with a baby voice too much and ask of him too much, like request that he not be a fucking asshole and that he be a normal and functioning part of someone's family dynamic or something, and maybe he just wasn't ready to deal with that sort of commitment and this was his way of making it known, running off to god knows where in search of something as unbeknownst to him as everyone else, distancing himself from the whole situation under the guise of Pursuing Something or Looking For Something, when all he was doing was Running Away again.

—grabbing at his neck like they do in the movies, trying to press both hands against the impressive leak that's sprung cheerfully from his thumping—

"CMERE DITCH!" My phone is really having a bad day, I toss it into the shadow of a bush near the house and cup my hands around my mouth. "CMERE BUDDY!" The storm has died down a little, I hear just rain instead, cold rain and the occasional bull-rush of wind, and I step in the direction of the ditch, and I'm whistling, trying to pierce the darkness with a sharper, higher note, and my foot slips a little and I almost go down, but I drop to a knee just in time, and my hands shoot out in front of me, sliding on squeaky wet grass *as I try to keep myself from keeling over into the squeaking tufts of ditch weeds—some sort of something still squeaking down there, probably something fucking rabid—*

And there he is. Maybe ten feet away, close enough that I can see his bastard eyes glinting sharply in the dark, his tiny snout glistening like the faraway nose of a car with a headlight out. At least, I think it's him, I find myself hoping it's him—what if it's a possum, what if it's a fucking *goblin* or something—as I crawl a little deeper into the ditch, as I push past dark tufts of wet weeds, toward the eyes, waiting for them to vanish at any moment, dart away; but they cower, the eyes—because they *are* eyes, and a nose—and they dip a little beneath my reaching grasp, timid and scared and wet and in need, and I quite suddenly feel like a gigantic piece of shit. My hand lands on the shivering bundle of wet fur, and I pick him up, and tuck him into my chest and fold my arms around him, and I climb back up the side of the ditch, slipping only a couple times, and back into the front yard and then across it, and I climb the stoop and pass through the front door, shutting it behind me and snapping the locks into place.

I'm toweling him dry in the bathroom, trying to stay between him and the toilet lest he be driven mad with that unexplainable desire to take a dip therein. He doesn't respond much to my ministrations, aside from some violent shivering, but I get him dry as best I can, and I wrap him up in the towel like a little burrito, and I tuck him under my arm, a furry football.

"You're alright, little fella," I say gently, or what feels like gently. He shivers really hard a couple times, but then stops. "No thanks to me, I know, but...you're alright."

You should keep him.

I strike the Heisman pose, a la star running back for the whatevers, and almost slip to my death on the bathroom tile. Epiphanies and sudden desire to not be a total piece of shit aside, I don't find myself suddenly wanting to keep him.

The same way you didn't feel whatever you'd expected to feel when you saw Luna for the first time?

Maybe it's like that, something that needs work. Maybe it would take time, but eventually it would click, and we'd be best friends or something, and shortly after I'd probably find myself combing Craigslist for not-so-murdery pet adoption ads, looking for a friend for him, or maybe down at the local shelter, rescuing *another* from this treacherous world; and then I start to panic a little at the thought of *another,* but I laugh a little, too, because there's not a fucking chance I'm keeping the one I've got, much less *another*. Besides, it's nothing I have to fret over right now, tonight, or even tomorrow, because if the deluge of responses had been any indication, I won't have a hard time rehoming him.

Assuming that's ultimately what I end up doing.

"But you know what they say about assumptions," I tell the kitten, raising him up and looking him right in his crazy little eyes. "You're an asshole and so am I."

I tuck him again and walk down the hallway, and back through the house, the floor complaining every step of the way. I pull open the door to the basement and walk gingerly down the dark steps and across the cold floor, and I click the light on, and it shines like H.C. Andersen's Emperor. The storm has picked back up outside, it sounds like distant applause down here. The boxes are where they were the last time I was down here, stacked next to the stairs with a crooked cat tree, and I flip open the flaps with my free hand and pull out a large, dank pillow the color of chewed bubble gum.

"Look," I say to the kitten under my arm, and I jiggle the pillow in the air just in front of him. "It's a pet bed. Perfect." I snort. "It's *purr*fect. Pun intended."

He doesn't appear to think I'm very punny, but it's hard to judge through his drooping eyelids. I take him back upstairs and put the bed in front of the couch, and I punch the pillow a couple times before placing him gently in the little hollow, where he curls up, even purring a little bit, I think, and he's asleep almost instantly, or doing a very good job at pretending so he can murder me the second I close my eyes.

"Gnight, Ditch," I whisper. He opens one eye very slightly, and the lid drifts slowly back down. "Do me a favor and stay out of the fucking toilet."

And he sighs heavily, as if he's had quite enough of my shit for one day, and the feeling is mutual, so I leave him there, and I head to my room—trudging now, pretty fucking tired now—and I fall face-first onto my bed, landing with a symphony of bouncing squeaks and a heavy sigh of my own.

You should keep him.

CHAPTER NINETEEN

"*My mind is tellin' me noOoOo,*" I warble, tipping back in my chair a little. The windows are open, and a cool night breeze is blowing in from the east, and with it comes the scent of outside: damp and cool greens, and warm yellows and browns, the smell of *out there*. Cars pass outside, tires whishing down the road to hither and yon, a tiny meep here and there, the occasional thumping of music. "But my *BODY*—" I put some bass in my voice, uttering the vowels with the back of my throat. "*My body is tellin' me yEeEeEs.*" The little clock radio in my room is giving all it's got, cranked to eleven and a little staticky, and a little too much tenor—R Kelly sounding like one of those underage girls he allegedly victimized—but it's either this or News from Lake Wobegon, the latter of which would have me nodding out in my chair instead of writing. "*I don't see nuthin' wroOoOOng...*"

But I do see something wrong, so I sit forward and backspace a few words, and then a sentence. A paragraph or two. And then I just sit there, hunched over like Quasimodo, and I stare at the word *the*, wishing the damn thing would spontaneously multiply, first in half, then those two halves in half again, and so on. It doesn't, of course, because it's not an exact science. It's pen to paper, man, it's fingers to the keyboard, sparks flying and getting your shit together and throwing paint at the canvas, it's all sorts of things that are much more subjective and much less scientific than meiosis.

I sigh and sit back in my chair. It creaks, and I hold my breath, praying the chair's cries for help don't lead to its *voluntary kicking of the fucking bucket or whatever*. But it holds. For now. I cross my arms and listen to the radio idly—R Kelly has spread his wings and flown away, now it's somebody trying to convince me that I've got mesothelioma—and I interrogate the *the* with my gaze for a little while before giving up and tipping back in my chair again.

It's been a week since Luna's birth. Since the dark and stormy night that followed. And since my last drink, too, which is worth noting, even if it's only because I've been broker than the American justice system, right up until this morning actually, when I'd cashed my first mccheck from my new job—the nondescript man emailing me to say, very nondescriptly, that he'd spoken with the owner of the mcplace, that they'd had a talk and decided that I was just the sort of person who needed this job so fucking bad that he'd keep showing up (my words, not his)—and *that* had been the real test, hadn't it, *that's* when I'd faced some real world applications—*that anxious feeling in your stomach forcing you to clench your jaws, hanging onto your sobriety with dear life as you try to make it out of the store*—but I'd done it, if only once so far, made it out of the store with nothing but a thin fold of bills in my pocket, mumbling the Declaration of Independence to myself while thinking about zebras fucking, anything to keep me from turning around *and going back and wrenching the cooler door open and grabbing just one or two,* and I'd made it, hopped on Frank—he's sporting some not-so-shiny new parts, courtesy of a roadside scavenge by yours fucking truly—and pedaled my ass off, and just kept pedaling and thinking about old documents and weird animal sex and trying to breathe, and eventually I'd gotten far enough away from the store that it would've been a serious pain to ride all the way back, or so I tell myself, and that'd been Day One, if anybody's keeping track.

I tilt my head and look up at the chipped stucco. The radio is assuring me that they play *all* of the hits, not just *some* of them like those other stations. It'd felt good to be tested and pass for once. But then I'd gotten home, opened the door, and walked into the empty house, and there'd been no one to tell, no one to celebrate this mini-victory with, to say *hey man, good fucking job*, and the urge had grown exponentially then, the thirst surging into my mouth like high tide, because it's evening, but it's still early evening, store's still open, I could be there in no time—Frank permitting—and buy just a couple drink just a couple, because I've gotta be up at the asscrack of dawn for work, so just a couple would be—

I stand up fast. The chair gives up and falls over completely, landing with a skip and a clatter. The peace shatters like Stone Cold is coming, and right on cue, Ditch comes skittering into the room, Tokyo-drifting across the wooden floor and into the wall, scrambling hard enough to put scratches down. He bumps the wall, only just, and then he's off again, tearing up the curtains and falling to the floor, and then up onto the couch, and I can hear his claws needling the cloth.

Not such an empty house after all.

"*Pispispis!*" I say. A flood of relief chills my bones, but my reflex is to flap my hands up and down at him—"Fucking *desist*, you bastard." He takes this as a challenge or something, and flings himself in my direction and begins attacking my feet with a primal ferocity, and then just as quickly, he's off again, down the hallway and into the bathroom, into the bedroom for some hot laps on the bed—the radio cuts off in the middle of the DJ telling me to call his hotline if I want to reque—into the hallway again, burbling and spitting away, and here he comes, bursting back into the room, hissing and spitting and walking sideways at me. And sure, my reflex is to tell him to fuck off somewhere else, but suddenly I'm laughing my ass off, I mean, genuinely laughing for the first time in forever, and I can't stop, no matter how offended he looks, not even when he rockets out of his battle stance and starts to scale me, needling my legs with tiny daggers and spitting up at me, daring me to laugh again, and I do, I'm almost in fucking tears and I don't know why. Maybe it's the absurdity of it all: this little bundle of orange fur attacking a big, tattooed bald guy, just giving him the *business*, feline vs felon; or maybe it's the relief, the sudden appearance of a distraction from the thirst that begins to gnaw on me every time I even *think* about taking another drink.

You should keep him. It might help you to feel less alone.

The laughter fades, but the smile stays. And it feels good. A little weird, but okay, I guess.

"You're lucky," I say, and I reach down and grasp him by the nape of his neck, wincing only a little as I pull him off me like a piece of stubborn Velcro. I raise him to eye level and lean back a little as he struggles against my grasp, his tiny legs whiplashing, his tiny maw snapping. "Or are you..."

Getting the job and having a source of income, becoming a contributing member of fucking society or whatever, it had made rehoming the kitten less of a priority. There were things going on in my life for once, *changes* happening, things to distract me from myself. It had certainly helped that my phone was deader than the dodo, cracked and rain-soaked, because there weren't constant buzzing reminders that I full-well intended on rehoming him. And a week passed while I wasn't looking, and he's still here, still being a pain in my ass, and always managing to distract me from myself in his own way, seemingly at times when I've really, *really* needed it.

"Fine, don't have a seizure," I say, and I deposit him on the floor and step back. He just sits there for a minute, looking dazed, maybe processing his hard-fought freedom. And then he perks up like he's taken a huge hit of crack or something, and he lays his ears back and makes a couple satanic noises and he's off again.

I pick the chair up and set it upright. It's seen better days.

But maybe he's not so lucky, being stuck here with me. Been here a week and he's still pissing in a paint pan and eating cheese popcorn. Fuck, I can rehome him anywhere, it won't be hard to find a nice family to take him, somewhere he can have a real litter box and real food and treats and toys and shit, I mean, that isn't this place, is it?

I sit down in the chair heavily. I reach for the computer and click out of Word, and I hover above the browser icon for a moment—*just click into your email real quick, it won't take five minutes to find him a home, just close your eyes and fucking point*—and I will myself to click it, it really will take only a few minutes, I'll be in bed and battling my soberness in no time, but....

You should keep him.

I slam the laptop closed and lean back in the poor chair once again. I'm gonna rehome him. I *am*. But there's work tomorrow, and then Jessica is coming over with Luna for a visit, which will be my first time seeing them since the birth, and the *book*, the fucking *book* could use some work, too, especially now with an entire child to take care of, gotta sell the fucking book tomorrow, and all kinds of shit.

You should—

I should go to bed, is what I should do. Because the question with the ditch kitty isn't merely to be or not to be rehomed. Just like the question with Luna isn't to be or not to be a father. No, the real question is more complicated. And so is the answer. And I've got my fucking hands full at the moment, and so it's just gonna have to wait until later on.

It's later on. I'm lying in bed, trying to sleep and not having much luck. Staring at the squeaky ceiling fan and wondering idly if it's worth it to get up and shut it off. From the sounds of things, Ditch has decided he doesn't like the feng shui of the bathroom. Or the living room. Or the kitchen. And he has taken it upon himself to move a few things around, my own personal poltergeist. I'm awake because I'm sober, because I'm not completely sodden with cheap alcohol; but I'm also awake because I can't get the complicated question to stop bouncing around inside my skull in search of the oh-so-complicated answer.

Are you ready to live your life for someone other than yourself?

But that's the way it's been for so long, just surviving, and sometimes barely getting by, all you can do is concentrate on taking just one more breath, and then just one more, over and over again, until you get to a place in your life where you forget you're doing it. Because sometimes you're thankful for just that, being able to fucking *breathe*, sometimes that's enough. And you forget about other things, other people, and you just survive and breathe and do shit to look out for *you*, yourfuckingself, because if you don't do it, *who will?*

I close my eyes. I can hear the shower curtain being shredded to pieces. *Just fucking breathe, man...* The smell of outside is coming in through the open window, and I inhale through my nose, slow and steady, and exhale.

Even if I am willing to finally start asking some of the harder questions, it doesn't have to be right now....

207

I breathe. In. Out.

Work tomorrow...Then Jessica is bringing Luna over...Little visit...

I breathe. In. Out.

Things are okay...For the first time in a long time, The Kid thinks... *as the light fades on another day, he drifts, sliding deeply into a semicon-* *scious state where he is aware of the things that are going on around him,* *as well as the things that are going on inside him,* and slowly the sound of shredding shower curtains, shattering glasses, and falling lamps fades. I drift into a fitful sleep, my subconscious keeping me right on the brink of REM, but I'm sleeping, I'm drifting a little further away with each breath, and—*it starts with a rush, faint, distant. It sounds like running* *water and it is pleasant, lulling him into an even deeper state of sleep. As* *it grows, as the sound picks up, he realizes what it is. Wind. Wild gusts of* *ferocious wind that blind, deafen, and mute. The roar of the wind peaks* *and sometimes, only sometimes, he can fight it*—I struggle against the onslaught of yet another nightmare, trying to swim away from—*a giggle,* *just one to start us off, and not a pleasant one*—but the more I struggle, the deeper I sink. I try to move my arms, my legs, I try to pick my head up from the pillow, everything, anything, but—*the giggle is the final sign* *that he is here to stay, for better or worse*—there's no going back, I've reached the point of no return. I seek the outside world for something to cling to, but it's too quiet, and—*he must scream, he must do something* *to expel the blackness filling his mouth and his throat, to drown out the* *sound of the wind filling his ears, the sound of goblins chattering and* *giggling, he MUST*—

Suddenly, the worst smell assaults me, comes out of nowhere and punches me in the fucking nose. Hints of butthole and damp fur and hot breath, and in my head, I recoil, pulling away from it at first, but beggars can't be choosing, can they? So I fight my desire to pull away from that smell, the only thing left of the outside world, and I reach out for it, grab it, and I hold onto it for dear life, like a drowning man would a piece of driftwood, like a thirsty man might a glass of water, and I don't let go even when the source of the smell starts biting me with tiny, sharp teeth.

I open my eyes, blinking away the darkness, blinking away sweat and tears, and I'm back, I'm really back. Relief floods my body in a cold rush. I can move my legs again, my arms. I let the kitten loose, and he gives me a swift bite in return, then retreats a whole four inches from my face and just sits there, squatting on the bed like a tired orange sweater, staring at me like some creep.

"Thanks, Ditch," I say, truly meaning it. I reach out and pat him. "You still fucking stink. But...thanks. You little night goblin."

A ringing silence descends on us. *You little night goblin.* Why had I called him that? I run my hand down his back, from ears to tail, and he starts to purr. I feel it before I hear it, a soft vibration, and I smile a little. Because isn't he's just like the ones that have plagued The Kid since you-know-when, pestering me just like them, keeping me awake just like them? He's the definition of a night goblin, albeit maybe not such a terrible one.

His eyes close into thin slits, and his head droops, but that's what destroying a house will do to you. He stretches one good time and curls himself into a tight ball beneath my hand and falls right asleep, mere moments after biting the shit out of me, no less, leaving me—*just fucking breathe*—staring at the ceiling fan and wishing, among other things, that I had a beer.

I'm staring at the computer screen again. It's probably one a.m., and I've gotta be up for work in about three hours, the dirty asscrack of dawn. The house is quieter than a funeral parlor, sans the sobbing, bereft widow. I can hear the computer starting to overheat, it's no more dependable than Frank, and the occasional car passes, a late-night ride to fucking nowhere, and I picture them, the drivers, tired like me, staring blearily like me, sort of asleep and awake at the same time, twilight driving. And I wonder where they're going at such an hour. Why they aren't already there. And if they're as lonely as me.

I'd laid there for a while, eyes closed, my hand atop the night goblin, wishing I could sell my soul for even just some twilight sleep, wondering if the asshole next to me knows anybody looking for a soul to buy—a little beat up, but it runs—he looks like the type who would; but no matter what I did, what I imagined, the sleep evaded me, hovering just outside of reach, and eventually I'd lifted my hand slowly and slid out of the bed at an infinitesimally slow rate, holding my breath lest I awake him, and I'd tiptoed out of the room, testing the floor for creaks with a delicate carefulness all the way, until I'd reached the chair and sat myself down in it carefully—for once—and that's where I've been ever since.

The *the* leers at me. I threaten to delete him if he doesn't quit being so sassy, but it feels empty. The urge to procrastinate grows. I click out of Word and make eye contact with the browser icon—*since you're up, might as well see about this rehoming shit*—and I click it twice in rapid succession. My email is my home page, cutting out the middle man, as it were, and the second the page pops up and loads, I see that my phone taking a shit has had no impact on the number of responses rolling in. Close to a *thousand* responses to the rehoming ad, a mix of positive and negative responses. I scroll. And more positive than negative, it seems, as I click through email after email, scanning them quickly and moving on to the next—*I saw your rehoming ad and wanted you to know that it was so fuckin funny man*—*aw, he's cute, he doesn't look like an asshole at all*—and lots of emojis—*have you ever had a cat before, he sounds like a pretty normal kitten*—

I press my lips into a thin smile. *Pretty normal,* hell, maybe so, maybe this is just par for the course when it comes to night goblins.

—*that ad was HILARIOUS*—*I love you and that asshole kitty*—*did you ever end up rehoming him, I'd love to come meet him*—

But not all of it's positive. A majority, but not all. And I find myself scrolling past the nicer messages, immersing myself in the emails that don't have much nice to say.

THE KITTY IS NOT AN ASSHOLE, YOU ARE—*PLEASE LET ME COME GET THE KITTEN, HE DESERVES BETTER*—and so on. I'm drawn to these messages, and find myself clicking from one to the next, and each one makes me need a drink more than the last. I'm much better off going back to bed and pretending to sleep, but I can't pull myself away—*click-click-click*—*I'm writing to inquire about the kitten you posted on Craigslist. It seems like he'd be better off somewhere else, judging from the disgusting ad you posted about him, so instead of being a complete piece of shit, just give him to someone who*—

Click.

I exit out of the email, finally finding strength enough to pull myself away. The kitten in question comes sauntering out of the bedroom, I guess the angry clicking woke him up, and he puts his front paws on my leg, needling them with his claws, implying he wants to climb me, but just can't find the strength. I scoop him up and put him in my lap.

"What do you think," I say, trying to pet him and receiving a nasty bite for my troubles. "Should I give you to someone else? Someone who's not an asshole? Do you deserve better?"

Better. *Hell, maybe he does. But why does that mean he has to be rehomed? Can't he find* better *right fucking here? Can't I?*

"Maybe we all deserve a little better," I tell the night goblin, musing. He's trying to clean himself, rearing his head back like a snake and attacking the side of his neck with a small, rough tongue. I tap him on the top of his head with one finger, and he takes it as an affront, grabs the finger with his front paws and starts rabbit-kicking it. "But you're still an asshole, aren't you, no matter how many pretentious emails we receive to the contrary."

I sigh and click my way back to the Word document. The *the* is still there, he's the *real* asshole in all of this, and even *he* deserves better. I stare at him for a minute, giving him one more chance to *change*, to make and cause some sort of betterness in his own way. The night goblin clambers up onto my shoulder and perches there, glaring down at the *the* along with me, and after a moment, I give up, and I smack the laptop shut and remove it from the desk, and I pull out a piece of paper and a pencil, as Ditch starts to purr and bite my earlobe at intervals, and I begin to write.

The Kid's like three beers in—

EPILOGUE

I remember taking the ambulance to Cape Fear Valley Hospital the night of August 14, 2010. I remember being ushered to the back of the ambulance against any and all protest—*I'm fine, I'm fine*—and I remember not really knowing whether I was fine or not, not caring, to be honest, because the only thing I could think about was what one of the police officers had said to me right before they shoved me onto a gurney.

He's dead. You killed him.

I remember being in the ambulance with Paul to my left on his own gurney, he's holding my hand and saying something about everything being okay, and there's an EMT or something asking me all these different questions that I don't know how to answer and don't want to answer because the only thing I can think about is—

He's dead. You killed him.

And being rolled into the hospital and being asked more questions that I don't want to answer and answering them anyway, and thinking more about what the police officer had said, and sitting up and being told to lie back down but sitting up anyway, shielding my eyes because the lights are so bright, too bright, what the police officer had said, and different people walking in and out of the too-bright room wearing too-bright scrubs with too-bright attitudes. I remember the nurse, this comfortable black woman, she's asking me what happened and am I okay and what my pain level is and do I need this and that and who can they call for me, and I tell her I'm in pain, yes, I am in so much pain, my heart's constricting beneath tight coils of it, and she takes my hand and rubs it and watches me in an understanding way, only she doesn't understand because she doesn't know what I've done.

"He's dead," I whisper, and I begin to sob then, I can't help it. "I killed him."

"Killed who, sweetie," she says, nodding gently, urging me on, sympathetic, but aware and cognizant of everything I'm saying too, filing it away for her notes. "Who died?"

And I try to tell her who died, but I don't know exactly, and this is worse, I think, having taken a life so quickly and carelessly that I don't even know his name or who he is, and what about his family and friends, the people who love him, the people who have to wake up tomorrow and realize that a drunk driver, so careless and fucking stupid, has taken from them someone very dear, that someone they've never met has destroyed their life.

"I want to go back," I say instead, moaning and casting a hand over my face. "I want to go back and switch places with him, my god, *please.*"

I remember meaning it, really and truly meaning it, and saying it over and over again like maybe, just maybe, whoever is Upstairs would hear me and make an exception just this once, and I remember, amid all the pain, how selfish and narcissistic my regret was, how its mere existence only made things worse because it seemed to highlight, amongst other things, how still alive I was.

That next year after the accident was one of the hardest of my life, and deservedly so. I was officially charged with second-degree murder, which in North Carolina carries a minimum of twelve years in prison. After a four-year stint with the 82nd Airborne unit out of Fort Bragg, which included two deployments and numerous awards for stellar performance, I was summarily dismissed from my position and removed from the Army with a General Under Honorable discharge. I spent that next year going to court, speaking with lawyers, and coming to terms with what I had done and the repercussions that were to follow. I was almost certainly going to prison, something I could hardly even fathom, and when the first plea deal came down to the tune of seven years, I was a mess. Not only could I not fathom it, I couldn't accept it, I wouldn't, and not because I felt any less responsible for what I'd done, but because I was fucking scared, absolutely terrified. I spent countless hours researching prison, what it was like and the sort of people who went there and how to act in there, how to exist, and I couldn't picture myself making it through the system in one piece. I watched shows and read books and combed blogs and forums for tips, but none of what I found helped. If anything, it exacerbated the situation, and in the end, I had to push all of it out of my head and accept the only thing I could recognize as the truth: I had killed a man and there was a price to pay, and quibbling over the exact total of said price was going to help no one, least of all his family and his loved ones, who were left to seek solace in the fact that I would be taken to task. The justice system would see to it that I paid my dues.

And so, when the second plea deal was offered, a sentence of four years and change, I accepted it. It had been almost exactly a year since that night when I turned myself in, remanding myself into the custody of the North Carolina Department of Corrections, and I was standing in the courtroom in handcuffs when I met Felipe Ramirez's family for the first time. His mother and brother sat in the pews behind the prosecutor, tissues in hand, and never have I felt so small, so horrible, as I did standing there. But as the prosecutor read the charges and the details of the plea deal, as my lawyer listed various mitigating circumstances and pleaded for mercy on my behalf, I felt for the first time in a long time that I was doing the right thing.

Four years in prison might not seem like a lot of time, especially when paired with what I did. Some have received much more time than I did for the same thing; some have gotten much less for what might be considered more serious offenses, and I encountered plenty of both during my time behind bars. Perhaps four years isn't enough time to make up for taking someone's life, but then, neither is seven years. Or ten. Or twenty. Because this is a debt that cannot be repaid. It's like making the minimum payment on a credit card, doing just enough to keep your head afloat, and this is a struggle that will stay with me for the rest of my life.

But I can say this: It was enough to change me. It was enough to completely alter the direction of my life, enough to destroy entirely who I'd been, or rather, who I thought I was and who I thought I was going to be. It was enough to shape me as a person, to mold me into this something, whatever this is, that society finds so hard to accept. And that's the caveat, you see, because going to prison and doing time isn't the punishment. It's a purgatory, a violent and sick and twisted sort of limbo, and the idea conveyed to you during your stint is that everything resets when you're released, that your debt will have been paid and you will be provided a receipt and you will be able to move forward with what's left of your life. But that's simply not true. Because the real punishment doesn't start until you change out of your prison garb and walk out that gate, returning to society very much worse for wear, tainted and marked, and you realize very quickly that things have changed too much, that you sacrificed who you once were in order to survive, and now it's like you just don't fit or something. You became institutionalized because you had no choice, doing what you had to do to just get by, but because you changed to fit your environment, society will forever struggle to place you anywhere that doesn't have bars.

I didn't stop drinking the night I started writing this book. I've had a lot of Day Ones. It was too easy to start drinking again, to drown my problems in beer, because alcohol and drugs do offer a sort of respite from this life, a temporary respite, sure, but a respite, nonetheless. I mean, it's not like you're shooting heroin behind a dumpster, it's not like you're smoking crack or meth or anything like that, and all of it boils down to what's legal and what's not, when it comes to society's perception, anyway, and you convince yourself that because everyone else thinks it's okay, it actually *is* okay, and that all of your problems exist in *spite* of your addiction, not *because* of it.

What a most dangerous lie.

But I had the *desire* to quit, and the *desire* is what you truly need when it comes to this shit. You have to want it for yourself. To be better. Because no matter how many times I faltered, no matter how many mistakes I made, no matter how many Day Ones, the desire to be better was still there. The desire to grow instead of shriveling. To live a life defined by something other than my past. And I still struggle, because abstaining is an uphill battle that is waged anew every single day, every time you go into a store and leave without buying your usual, every time you go out to dinner and don't have a few drinks, every time you're at any number of hectic holiday family functions and you make that conscious decision—and it *must* be a conscious one—not to drink. Hell, sometimes it seems like I could pick up a drink at any moment, especially when shit gets hard, because it's what I know and it's what's easiest. But I've slowly gotten better at learning to accept my past for what it is without forgetting. Because it's equally important to me that I don't forget. You know what they say about forgotten history.

As I write this, I've been sober for over two years, quit drinking for good. *The Kid* hasn't seen hide nor hair of the night goblins in ages, save the furry kind. And the key was finding things that meant more to me than Drinking. It wasn't easy; I think quitting was one of the hardest things I've done, but I remain cognizant of my battle and stay prepared for those inevitable moments of weakness, and I concentrate as much as possible on the things in my life that mean more to me than Drinking.

Like Ditch.

Finding Ditch the Night Goblin changed my entire life. For the first time in forever, I had to think and care about someone other than myself, I had to look out for someone other than me. I had to feed the insatiable orange beast, change his litter, and clean up his messes. I had to give him attention and deal with the attention he gave me and, most importantly, I had to love him. I figured out early on in our relationship that love was the most important aspect of our bond, because without love, we were just two lost souls passing each other on the way to Somewhere Else. And this was important because right around the same time, I became a father. And everything changed again. Because while Ditch taught me how to love someone, Luna Rae taught me how to be loved. How to accept my own imperfections and love myself in spite of them, which was important if I was ever going to love anyone else. She taught me how to be a person, a *real* person, and she taught me how to move on from mistakes made, how to leave past things in the past and live in the moment, however fleeting. She taught me how to smile for real, laugh for real, and she taught me how to cry, how to accept and process the bad feelings along with the good. She taught me how to be a father, a pretty damn good one—laying to rest my fears of perpetuating a cycle of abuse—and she taught me that everything is going to be okay, no matter how not okay things seem sometimes.

But the change didn't stop there. I found Ditch and Jessica found me, rescued me, and she and I have added to our family time and time again over the past few years, giving me more reasons to continue to be better. We have four kids now, and yes, we did adopt *another* night goblin. *Twice.* Along with The Ditch Kitty, we now have Mr Wednesday, a one-eyed orange tabby, and Sirius Black, a complete doofus, and they're all assholes in their own way. And the Ditch Kitty rehoming ad that went viral has evolved into a magnificent catmunity of supporters that have been there for this felon and feline time and time again, through thick and thin. For once in *The Kid's* life, things are pretty great. And therein lies what might be the hardest part of this entire journey. Trying to reconcile my past with the present while making sure I don't forget how I got here. Forgiving myself is a battle I wage to this very day. And while I'm still not altogether sure I'm deserving of any sort of forgiveness, moving on from the past meant accepting my mistakes. Not forgetting. Accepting. Moving on. Growing. Causing change instead of waiting for it. Becoming someone other than who I thought I had to be. A better someone. None of which would've been possible without the help of a tiny orange fuckwhistle named Ditch. Which raises the question:

Who, in the end, saved whom?

ACKNOWLEDGEMENTS

Writing a book turned out to be much harder than *The Kid* ever imagined, and it wouldn't have been possible without a fantastic team behind me, pushing all the way.

To Jessica: Thank you for believing when no one else did, including myself. For taking me by the hand and leading me out of the dark. For giving me the moon. I love you, bug.

To Ron: Your support during this process never wavered, and sometimes our calls were all that kept me writing. Thank you.

To Emily: Thank you for reading this fucking thing over and over again. For snitching on me when it meant the most. *Cue GIF of Robert Redford nodding approvingly*

To Antoine Bouraly: Thank you for your patience, for reading the book at its very worst and somehow managing to illustrate exactly what I was trying to say.

To Harrison Demchick, Matt DeMazza, and Asya Blue: I think Stephen King said it best – To write is human, to edit is divine. Many thanks to each of you for your guidance during the very stressful post-writing process. If this book is actually worth a damn, it's because of y'all.

And last, but certainly not least, to Ditch's Bitches: I hope you're actually reading this. That you didn't skip it, I mean, isn't that what everyone does with a book's acknowledgements? Thank you to each and every one of you for being there for me and Ditch, through good times and bad, through the light and through the dark. Who knows where we'd be without y'all, without this fantastic catmmunity we've built. Because of y'all, we became more than just two assholes giving each other grief. Because of y'all, we became family. And it was because of y'all that we were even able to create this book! Over 800 people pledged $33,000 via our Kickstarter campaign to help bring this project to life, and I'm truly blessed to be able to thank some of you by name:

JC Witherspoon, Tabitha Saltzman, Sheena Linares, Ciana Peil, Michele Braidwood, Kathryn Anderson, Dave Ledbetter, Lisa Gioventu, Big Werm, Brenda Nemeth, Nakia Johnson, Matt Kost, Andi LePore, Michelle Bartelt, Kelley Korona & Marc Robinson, Jessica Thompson, Cheesecake Queen, Andrea Love, Deena Barrett, Caitlin Holly, Deandrea Pinkney, King Piggens aka Big Sexy Boi, Celeste (Koobecaf) Place, Melissa Winans, Kristie Elizondo, Traci L. Busha, Carmen Jacobson, Jessica Fritz, Michael M Tallman, COL(R), Lena Gudell, Kristy Curpenski, Nicole Seifert, Erin Hudgins, Josie the Cat and Julie Smith, Donna Hendges, Pamela Ferrell, Lindsey & Layla Macit, Cat Owens, The Howards, Linda Lane, Kaelyn Stafford, Taylor and Marissa Fuller, Linn Stewart, Jennifer Learman & her furbabies(Ollie & Lucy), Linda & Alexis Caffrey, Frankie Villar and Cooper, Victoria Campbell, Brittany Durham, Lee Ann Erickson, Jenny Hammack, Kristina Schwartz, Stephanie Champ, Karen DeVore, Jen Westmoreland, Michael Barth, Debra Demuro, Martha Lea, Natasha Dubois, Jennifer Perry, LuAnn Eaton, Juls & Patches & Phoebes, Danielle-Ashley-Michael-Alexandria-Blue-Kimchi-Rorschach-Morgan-Danica-Kaiju-Berlioz-and-Sparta Brunow, Melinda Rose, Ashton-Cali-Shelly-and-Cheeto Lee, Linda Opella, Karen Dirichleau, Becky Corbett, Carolyn George-Reeder, Jolene Destefano, Barbra Burke, Spud & Frankie Mallender, Michelle Berkemeier, Amber Pardeik, Stacy Varnadoe, Geralyn Pelle, Patricia Grimes, Susan Anguiano, Jamie Cunningham, Alicia Murray, Amanda Lehman, Stephanie Rodgers, Marci (Janssen) Ludwig, Penny Myers-Prince & Mark Prince, Denese Van Over, Sara Kelly, Shayne & Emi, Melissa Metivier, Jeni Daniel, Courtney P Rouse, Tiffany Noelle Meyer & Ralph Ewing Paris IV, Bob & Joan Schultz, Samantha Petersen, Diane J (Dee Jaye MamaCat) Hall, Melissa Hutchinson, Amber Eichorn, Shannon Luptowski, Doug & Kimberly Wilde, The Bimbo, Lauren Songer, Katelyn Ruggles, Rebecca Zollman, Just Another of King Ditch's Bitches, Dalene Becerra, Sam C & Kitten & Fat Peter, Julie Polley & Family, Lauren Rose, Stephanie Kelley, Megan Ramsey, Laurie Robb, Sheila Wilson, Penny Dreadful the Cat, Jen H, Katrina Fidalgo, Dawn New, Kara Adrian, Rachel Smith, Chelsea Claytor, Maryam AF, Parker Banfield, Heather R Smith, Cassie-Schroedie-Einstein-Newton Repp, Nikki Schram, Leah Christian, Mary G Marker, Batman & QuinnHarley & Poison Ivy & Penguino, Shannon Schillings, Kristin A Peters, Christy Rach, Wylde Phoenix Leather, Kelly Loyzelle, Helen Goulden, Megan

Vinitsky, Trace & Shalynda, Beth Voigt, Jacqueline J, Lola & Jasper & Oliver & Mimi, Jessica Dietzler, Christy Howell, Bonnie Hoover, Alejandro Merino & Cupcake, Mandy Porter, Shelly Wright, Roni Nixon, Rochelle McLemore, Lynn Dakin, Katrina & Erin Trickler, Kishella JoStarr Roelof, Justine Mikaloff, M & E & Z Irish, Ammarina & Maggie, Michelle Kile, Eric J Freier, Erica Bowles, Kimberly Summers, Tammy Webb, Kayla Dawn Mansil, Grammy Marlene & Chelsy & Nate & Charli, Jamie Lynn G, Kaelleyn & Kyme, Dawn Greenwood, Megan Siegmann, Sharon Meerbaum Dunn & Lola & Sonny, Lindsay M Beaver, Lou Ann Smith, Elizabeth A Macias, Pamela Maggio, Loren Chouinard & Matt Przystas, Melody Shaw, Terri Foster, Valerie Strunk-Ditch's Bitch From The Start, PJ Blain, Samantha Kirkpatrick, Beccy Jones, John & Tia & Aaron & Finn, Jill Hendrickson, Holly Renée Wheeler, Sara Jo Solooki, Vikkie Ashbeck, Ilona Chodnicka, Debbie Link, Kathryn Schaefer, Shannon Boggs Champion, Amy Krueger, Dawn Brown, Marla Trail, Cat Brooks-Farmer, Melissa Harvey, Andria Jolly-Morris, Tina Dion, David & Jeanette & Bryan Sims, Linda-Patty, Kathy Groves, SewBlest, Kenzie Allen, Patrick & Courtney Graham, Tim Schramm, Shelia Lyle, Stacy Krupco, Allison Yopp, Heather Blazer, Charlotte R Maher, Amanda Carmelia, Justine Mikaloff & Jeff Vealey & Luna the Husky & Bindi Super-Kitty, Marci Hawkins, Jacqui Raghib-Trail, Becky Ross, Joseph Thor Schafer, Barbie Skelton, Kristy Holt, Stephanie Scammahorn, Duke & Leah, Moeller Family, Pat & Jennifer Falk, Erin Petit, Ginny & Mindy Studley, Craig & Darlene Coonts, Sabrina Jacobs, Carolyn Milvet, Michelle Privette, Caitlin & Daniel Brion, Kimberly Landis, S Miyamoto, Erica Christiansen, Randall Law & Lauren Poole, Cindy DeWitt, Samantha Dunn, Katie Langdon, Claire White, JR Schaefer, Kimberly Price, Victoria Grams, Crystal Caluori, Damian Winn, Connie DiSanto, Kristy Rasmussen-Vincent, Valerie Keolani, Katheryne Doyle Stead, Carrie Richardson, Stephanie Roundy, Melissa Treusch, Laura Medina, Erin Harris, Georgeanne K Musson, Malinda Gee, Marcie Ann Blair, Kimberly L Esse, Paul & Susan Wood Family, Sarah Ross, and Sue Simo.

And while it certainly makes for an intimidating wall of text, these names are merely a small portion of the support we received from Ditch's Bitches. Thanks for everything, y'all. You've truly been a family to *The Kid*. AND LOOK, WE DID IT!

NOTE FROM THE AUTHOR

I truly hope you enjoyed reading this book. I know parts of it are quite dark, maybe a little hard to read, but I shared pieces of myself that have never seen the light of day. I took chances, maybe too many. And I want to sincerely thank you for walking through the shadows with me. I really hope we never have to go back. But I have a feeling we will.

If you have a moment, I'd love if you left a **review on Amazon**! Reviews are gold to a lowly indie author like myself, and I'd be forever grateful if you took a moment to tell me what you thought about the book.

Go to **jtgregory.com** to get on our mailing list for updates on future works by JT Gregory, and don't forget to follow our social media accounts for updates on what The Ditch Kitty is up to these days!

Facebook: @ditchthenightgoblin, @officialJTGregory

Instagram: @ditchthenightgoblin

Twitter: @realJTGregory